# Quick Wits
## AND
# Nimble Fingers

## BERNICE WELLS CARLSON

*Dolores Marie Rowland,*
*illustrator and art advisor*

Abingdon/Nashville

**Library of Congress Cataloging in Publication Data**

CARLSON, BERNICE WELLS.
 Quick wits and nimble fingers.
 Includes index.
 SUMMARY: Presents 10 folk tales from around the world accompanied by
 23 related crafts.
 1. Tales. [1. Folklore. 2. Handicraft] I. Rowland, Dolores Marie. II.
 Title.
 　　　PZ8.1.C2Qi　　　　[398.2]　　　　79-10035

ISBN 0-687-35199-5

## Acknowledgments

"Big Long Man and the Giant," from *Navajo Winter Nights* by Dorothy Hogner. Adapted by permission of the publisher, Thomas Nelson, Inc., © 1935 by Dorothy Childs Hogner.

"Bread for a Fighting Giant," adapted from "The Legend of Knockmany" in *Celtic Fairy Tales* by Joseph Jacobs.

"Enty Merchants, Erith Robbers," adapted from "Pride Goeth Before a Fall," in *Indian Fairy Tales* by Joseph Jacobs.

"The Fisherman and the Genie," retold from *Arabian Nights.*

"The Jackal's Lawsuit," reprinted from *The Fire on the Mountain and Other Ethiopian Stories* by Harold Courlander and Wolf Leslau, by permission of Holt, Rinehart and Winston, Publishers. Copyright 1950 by Holt, Rinehart and Winston. Copyright © 1978 by Harold Courlander and Wolf Leslau.

"Juan Malo and His Magic Rod," based on stories found in *Chamorro Legends on the Island of Guam,* collected and translated by Mavis Warner Van Peenen, under the auspices of the Micronesian Area Research Center, University of Guam, Agaña, Guam, M.I., and used with their kind permission.

"One Man's Horse," reprinted from "A Turkish Judge" in *Folklore from Foreign Lands* by Catherine T. Bryce, Newson & Co., New York, 1913.

Dedicated to
**CATHERINE BRITT CARLSON**
and
**JENNIFER STORY ROWLAND**

# *Thank You*

First of all, I wish to thank my art advisor and illustrator, Dolores Marie Rowland. Together, we researched the cultures of the areas from which the stories came, trying to analyze the skills and the spirit of the art work of the people. Together, we chose art and craft projects related to the stories and the cultures, within the scope of the abilities and interests of children in the middle grades and older.

Both she and I thank the many children who have heard us tell stories and have done art projects similar to those in the book—children in recreation, church, and library programs, at day and residential camps, Cub Scouts and Girl Scouts, in schools, at home, and other places. We would like especially to thank members of the Wise Owl Book Club of the Frederick Douglass Liberation Branch of the Franklin Township Library, New Jersey. Under the guidance of their director, Jacqueline Cody, and their storyteller, Yvonne Caesar, they took part in summer programs combining stories and related art work similar to the style of this book.

We would also like to thank librarians, teachers, and other friends who helped us develop the book, especially: Sister Felicia Plaza, M.M.B., Micronesian Area Research Center, Guam; Mavis Van Peenen, Long Beach, California; Christine Umberger, Springfield, Virginia; Estelle Resta, Lois Howe, David Rowland, and Carl W. Carlson, all of Franklin Township, New Jersey; and Helen Cooke, Bellevue, Washington.

# Contents

# *Preface*

What do you do when you get in a jam? Slug it out? Give in? Or use your wits to outsmart your adversary?

Characters in the following folktales find themselves in terrifying, or at least perplexing, situations. The problem may be:

How can I get out alive?

How can I solve a problem?

How can I get justice?

or

How can I avoid big trouble?

Read or listen to a story. Think about the characters. Ask yourself, "What would I have done if I had been there?"

Think about the place, long ago, and sometimes far away. Then do an art or craft project that reminds you of a character or of the land where the story takes place.

You can read a story to yourself and then work alone.

Or you can listen to a story and then do art or craft work, as a member of a group in a recreational, church, camp, or library program, or at school, or at home. If you have a place to store your art work, you need not complete a project in a single day.

As you read and work, have fun. Use your imagination to bring together the world of folklore and the world of arts and crafts.

# 1

## *Enty Merchants,*
## *Erith Robbers*

Long ago, there lived in India ten cloth merchants who always traveled together. As they worked with each other, they developed a secret code that enabled them to talk in the presence of a buyer without revealing the lowest price at which an item might be sold.

If a buyer refused to pay twenty rupees for a length of cloth, a merchant might ask his partner, "What's our lowest price for this cloth?"

The second merchant might look at the cloth, feel it, consider the matter, act as if he hated to sell the cloth at a loss, and mumble, "Enty rupees," meaning ten rupees.

The buyer, who couldn't understand the secret-code word, might offer fifteen rupees, or some other amount, and purchase the cloth, unless, of course, he offered less than ten rupees. The system worked very well, and the merchants prospered.

As the merchants grew richer, they traveled farther and farther afield, making more and more money on each trip. When they were returning home from one such trip, laden with money and a few remaining bags of merchandise,

11

they came to a cool, inviting forest with one well-traveled path running through it—a pleasant place to walk during the heat of day.

Down the path the merchants ambled, single file, each enjoying his own dream of what he would do with his new wealth, each completely unaware of the fact that in this forest there lived three notorious robbers.

When the merchants reached the middle of the woods, the three robbers suddenly appeared. With raised cudgels and swords, they ordered the merchants to lay down all they had.

What could the merchants do? They had no weapons. They dropped their bags of money and cloth.

Then the robbers commanded the merchants to undress down to their loincloths.

Still the merchants felt defenseless. One by one, each man disrobed and stood, humiliated, with his fellow traders.

The robbers laughed and laughed, as loud as they could. The sight of the ten pompous men standing huddled together, wearing only loincloths, made them proud. They, three robbers, had overcome ten wealthy merchants, plundered their property, and made them stand near-naked. Why not carry the jest farther, one robber suggested. Treat the stuffy merchants like fools. Make them dance!

"Agreed!" his cohorts said. Whereupon, the three robbers seated themselves regally before the merchants, and raising their swords, ordered them to dance.

Nine of the merchants cowered before the robbers and mourned their fate. They had lost their wealth, even their clothing. They were forced to stand in the presence of other men, wearing only loincloths. Yet the robbers were not satisfied. They commanded them to dance. Why should well-traveled merchants dance like fools before robbers? "Alas! Our fate!" they sighed. "Alas!"

The tenth merchant wasted no time in moaning. He considered the situation carefully, pondering the loss of money and clothing, the dance they no doubt would have to perform, and the arrogant manner in which the robbers had seated themselves on the grass.

The nine merchants began to dance a sluggish shuffle. The robbers jeered at them, and then, placing their weapons on the ground, pulled out bags of betel nuts so they might chew as they enjoyed the spectacle.

At that moment, the tenth merchant dashed away from the group and began to dance with great leaps in a circle around the robbers. As he danced, he sang a strange song in a false voice, like a cry from the distant jungle.

> We are enty men.
> They are erith men.
> If each erith men
> Surround eno man,
> Eno man remains.
> Ta! Tam! Tom! Tadinganna!

The song meant nothing to the robbers, who were watching the leaping leader, not trying to understand the words of his song.

13

But the nine other merchants got the message. In their code, it meant:

> We are ten men.
> They are three men.
> If each three men
> Surround one man,
> One man remains
> To tie them up!

The nine merchants stopped their sluggish shuffle. They, too, began to leap around the robbers in a large circle. They followed their leader as he invented new rhythms. As the merchants danced, the leader repeated his strange song three times.

The robbers were overcome with laughter. Never had they imagined anything so funny as these ten potbellied

merchants leaping like demons, shimmying like belly dancers, gyrating like men of the jungle.

The robbers howled, clapped in time to the rhythms, and swayed back and forth as if they were in a trance. The merchants danced on and on, the circle getting smaller and smaller, closer and closer to the robbers.

Suddenly the leader let out one wild, piercing cry—"Owny!" (Now!)

The merchants quickly separated into groups of three. Each group surrounded a robber and pinned him to the ground. The leader opened a bag, ripped pieces of cloth into strips, and securely bound each robber—feet, arms, and eyes and mouth for good measure. The robbers lay on the ground like three bags of rice.

The merchants lost no time. Hurriedly, they scooped up their clothing, their bags of money and cloth, and the robbers' cudgels and swords. Down the path they fled, until they emerged from the forest, a strange looking, but triumphant, group of men.

*(A tale from India retold)*

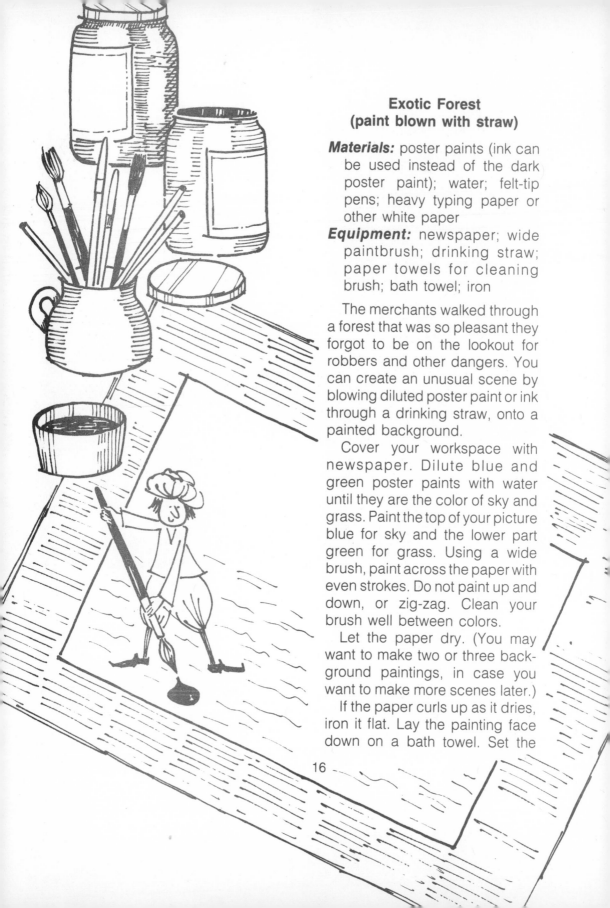

## Exotic Forest
## (paint blown with straw)

**Materials:** poster paints (ink can be used instead of the dark poster paint); water; felt-tip pens; heavy typing paper or other white paper

**Equipment:** newspaper; wide paintbrush; drinking straw; paper towels for cleaning brush; bath towel; iron

The merchants walked through a forest that was so pleasant they forgot to be on the lookout for robbers and other dangers. You can create an unusual scene by blowing diluted poster paint or ink through a drinking straw, onto a painted background.

Cover your workspace with newspaper. Dilute blue and green poster paints with water until they are the color of sky and grass. Paint the top of your picture blue for sky and the lower part green for grass. Using a wide brush, paint across the paper with even strokes. Do not paint up and down, or zig-zag. Clean your brush well between colors.

Let the paper dry. (You may want to make two or three background paintings, in case you want to make more scenes later.)

If the paper curls up as it dries, iron it flat. Lay the painting face down on a bath towel. Set the

16

regulator on the iron for wool or warm. Iron the paper gently.

Cover your workspace with newspaper. Prepare poster paint or ink the shade you want for tree trunks. It may be black, or brown, or brown with a little black added. The paint should be well-thinned with water.

Using a paintbrush, put a big drop of dark paint on your background paper at the place where you would like to have the base of a tree trunk. Through a drinking straw, blow the drop of paint toward the painted sky. When the trunk of the tree is as high as you want it, blow the remainder of the original drop of paint in different directions at the top of the tree, for branches.

Plan where you would like to have a path in the picture. As you drop the paint for more trees, leave space among the trunks for the imaginary path. Branches may cross the open space.

When the paint is dry, use felt-tip pens to paint flowers and leaves on the branches.

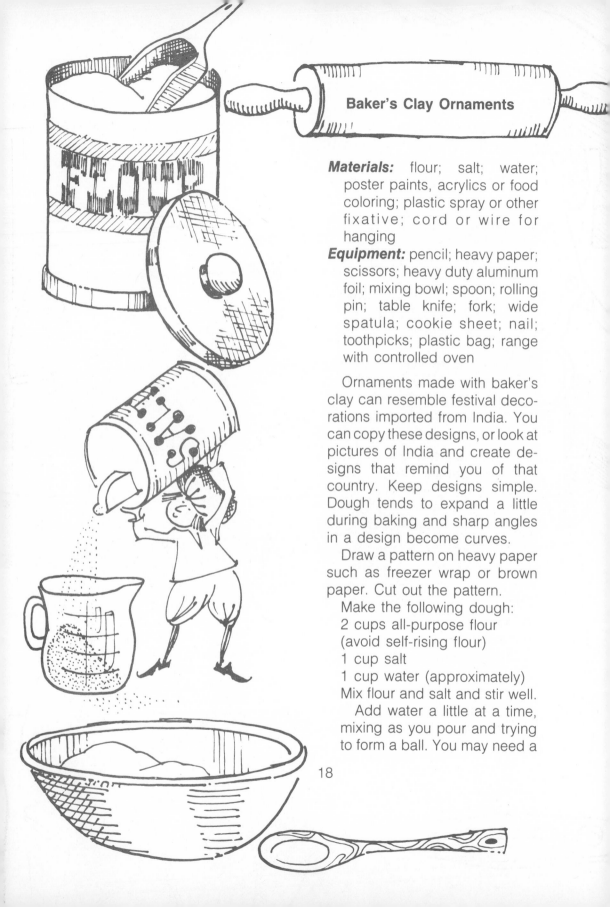

## Baker's Clay Ornaments

**Materials:** flour; salt; water; poster paints, acrylics or food coloring; plastic spray or other fixative; cord or wire for hanging

**Equipment:** pencil; heavy paper; scissors; heavy duty aluminum foil; mixing bowl; spoon; rolling pin; table knife; fork; wide spatula; cookie sheet; nail; toothpicks; plastic bag; range with controlled oven

Ornaments made with baker's clay can resemble festival decorations imported from India. You can copy these designs, or look at pictures of India and create designs that remind you of that country. Keep designs simple. Dough tends to expand a little during baking and sharp angles in a design become curves.

Draw a pattern on heavy paper such as freezer wrap or brown paper. Cut out the pattern.

Make the following dough:
2 cups all-purpose flour
(avoid self-rising flour)
1 cup salt
1 cup water (approximately)
Mix flour and salt and stir well.

Add water a little at a time, mixing as you pour and trying to form a ball. You may need a

18

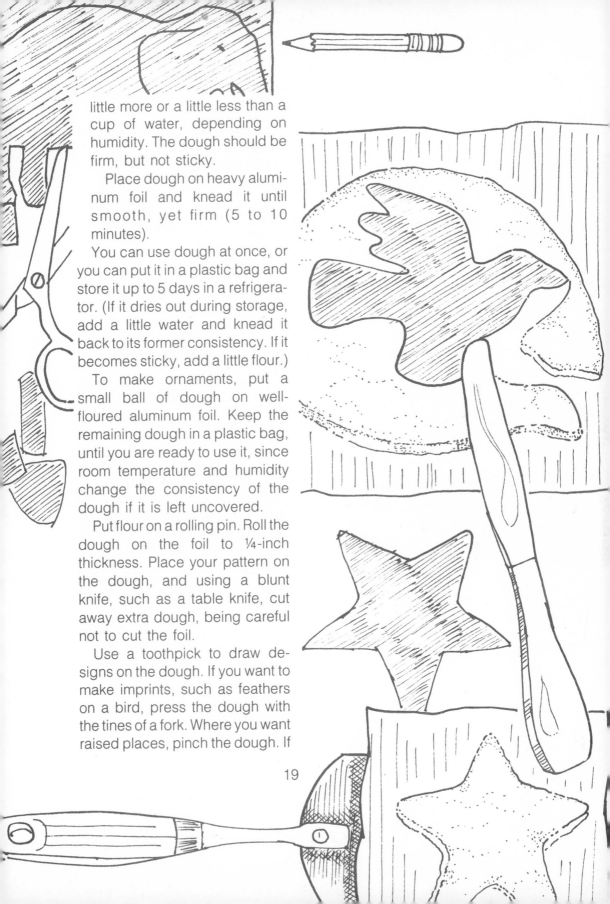

little more or a little less than a cup of water, depending on humidity. The dough should be firm, but not sticky.

Place dough on heavy aluminum foil and knead it until smooth, yet firm (5 to 10 minutes).

You can use dough at once, or you can put it in a plastic bag and store it up to 5 days in a refrigerator. (If it dries out during storage, add a little water and knead it back to its former consistency. If it becomes sticky, add a little flour.)

To make ornaments, put a small ball of dough on well-floured aluminum foil. Keep the remaining dough in a plastic bag, until you are ready to use it, since room temperature and humidity change the consistency of the dough if it is left uncovered.

Put flour on a rolling pin. Roll the dough on the foil to ¼-inch thickness. Place your pattern on the dough, and using a blunt knife, such as a table knife, cut away extra dough, being careful not to cut the foil.

Use a toothpick to draw designs on the dough. If you want to make imprints, such as feathers on a bird, press the dough with the tines of a fork. Where you want raised places, pinch the dough. If

19

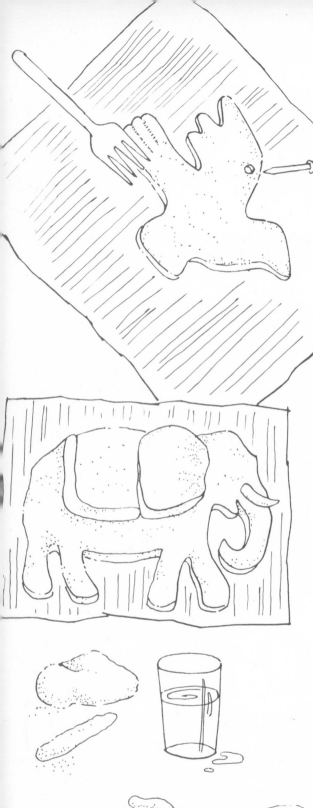

you want to build up the basic figure, put flour on your hands and roll a small piece of dough into the shape you need. Moisten the edges of the additional dough with water and press it onto the basic pattern.

With a nail, make a hole through the top of the ornament so that you can hang it later.

Leaving a wide margin, cut away the extra foil on which the dough ornament is resting. Slip a wide spatula under the foil and carefully place the foil and cutout dough on a cookie sheet.

Turn control of oven to 325°. As soon as you have filled the cookie sheet, or used up your dough, put the sheet holding the shapes into oven and bake 30 minutes for every ¼-inch of thickness. Remove the sheet from oven and test shapes to see if they are baked. If necessary, return to oven and bake a little longer.

When the ornaments are cool, paint them with poster paints, acrylics, or diluted food coloring. When that basic coat is dry, you may add colorful spots, or paint certain portions with diluted glue and sprinkle on sparkle.

When dry, coat the ornament with plastic spray or some other fixative.

20

Put a decorative cord or a wire through the hole in the top.

*Note:* A small amount of glycerine added to the basic dough makes it more elastic and somewhat easier to handle. But glycerine is expensive and not really necessary. If you do want to use glycerine, add a little before you add all the water, since less water will be needed.

# 2

## *The Jackal's Lawsuit*

Leopard and Jackal went out together to hunt. On the edge of a village where Man lived they captured some game. Leopard captured a goat, but Jackal captured a cow. They drove their prizes home and put them in the field to pasture.

Leopard was not happy that Jackal's animal was so much larger than his own. In the night he went again to look at them in the pasture, and he found that Jackal's cow had given birth to a calf. He was overcome with envy. So he took the calf away from the cow and tethered it with his goat.

In the morning he went to Jackal and said: "How lucky I am! This morning I went to the field, and what do you think? My goat has given birth to a calf!"

"That can't be," Jackal said, "for a goat can only give birth to a kid."

"Come for the proof," Leopard said. He took Jackal to the field where the calf was tethered with the goat.

"Now you can see for yourself I have spoken the truth," Leopard said.

"Since only a cow can give birth to a calf, the calf is mine," Jackal said.

"Do you see the proof and continue to argue?" Leopard said. "Can't you see the calf with my goat?"

"Yes, I see her," Jackal said. "But even if I saw her standing with an elephant, still she would be mine."

They argued this way until at last Leopard said, "Let us be judged! Others will recognize that justice is on my side!"

So they went in search of judges, and the first one they found was Gazelle. Leopard told his story, and Jackal told his, but Gazelle was afraid of Leopard, as were most animals of the bush.

"You see how it is," Jackal said. "It is clear that the calf is mine."

Gazelle looked at Leopard and was frightened. He put on his most learned look, and cleared his throat and said:

"Well, when I was young it was true that only cows had calves. But times have changed. The world moves on. Now, as you can see, it is possible for goats to have calves. This is my judgment, as Heaven is my witness!"

They went to Hyena, and told their story again. But Hyena, too, was afraid of Leopard, so when Jackal was through making his complaint, Hyena said, with an anxious look on his face:

"I have come to the conclusion that ordinary goats cannot have calves, but goats that are owned by leopards can. That is my judgment, as Heaven is my witness!"

All of them, Leopard and Jackal, Gazelle and Hyena

went to the place of Antelope, and once more the argument was carried on. Antelope listened in worried silence, and when they were through he said with a learned air:

"Once it was the law of all living things that each one should bear only his own kind. Lions bore lions, goats bore goats, and camels bore camels. But the law has been changed. It is now permitted for goats to bear calves. This is the truth, as Heaven is my witness!"

"Since there are no more judges, the calf is clearly mine," Leopard said.

"There is still Baboon," Jackal said, so all of them went together to the rocky place where Baboon lived.

They found him turning over stones to get at the ants and grubs that lived there.

"Judge our case," Leopard said, and then both Leopard and Jackal told their stories. Baboon listened with a far-off look in his eyes. When they were through they waited for his judgment. He slowly climbed to a high rock and looked down at them. But he said nothing. He held a small stone in his hand and plucked it with his fingers.

"Well?" Leopard said impatiently. "You see how it is. What is your verdict?"

"Wait," Baboon said. "Can't you see I am busy?"

"What are you doing?" Leopard asked.

"I have eaten my meal, and now I must play a little music before I judge," Baboon said.

"Music? What music?" all the animals asked.

"Here, the music I am playing on this instrument!" Baboon replied with irritation.

"Ha! He plucks upon a stone!" Leopard said. "Look what a stupid person we have asked to judge for us! No music can come from a stone!"

Baboon looked at Leopard.

"If a calf can come from a goat, surely sweet music can come from a stone?" he asked.

Leopard was embarrassed.

"Hm. What lovely music," he said.

The other animals shouted:

"It is true! As Heaven is our witness, only a cow can have a calf!"

And so because the community was united against him, Leopard returned the calf to Jackal.

*(An Ethiopian tale)*

## Aluminum Foil Relief

**Materials:** heavy cardboard from carton; lightweight cardboard, such as suit box or cereal box; heavy-duty aluminum foil; heavy-duty household glue; India ink or black shoe polish

**Equipment:** scissors; pencil; newspapers; paintbrush; steel wool

Burnished foil relief pictures have the appearance of hammered metal. They can be geometric shapes, perhaps representing the mountains and stones of Ethiopia, or they can be more realistic figures.

Cut a piece of heavy cardboard for a background, the size you want the finished picture to be. Plan your picture. You may want to draw it on the background. Cut lightweight cardboard into the shapes you plan to use (rocks, mountains, people, animals). Arrange them on the background. If you wish, place smaller pieces of cardboard on top of these to build up the relief. When you have a design you like, glue the pieces in place.

Cut a piece of heavy-duty aluminum foil larger than the background. Brush the entire cardboard picture, including the background, with a thin layer of heavy-duty glue. Fit the foil, shiny side down, over the picture. Carefully pat the foil in place. Rub it gently until the different levels of cardboard stand out. Fold the edges of foil in back of the cardboard, and glue them down.

Cover your workspace with newspaper, wear a smock, and still be very careful. Using a brush, coat the surface of the aluminum foil with India ink or black shoe polish. Let it dry. If you are using shoe polish, you may need to add an extra coat.

To bring out the highlights of the relief, rub the surface of the picture gently with steel wool.

## Stone Amulet

***Materials:*** small stone; green spool wire or other thin wire

The baboon in the story used a stone to produce pretend music. You can make a stone amulet, or charm, to wear as a pendant.

Find a pretty small stone. Wash and dry it well. Look at the stone and determine what kind of simple wire case you can make that will hold the amulet securely without hiding its natural beauty. Every stone produces a new challenge.

Use either colored spool wire or some other thin wire to make the case.

27

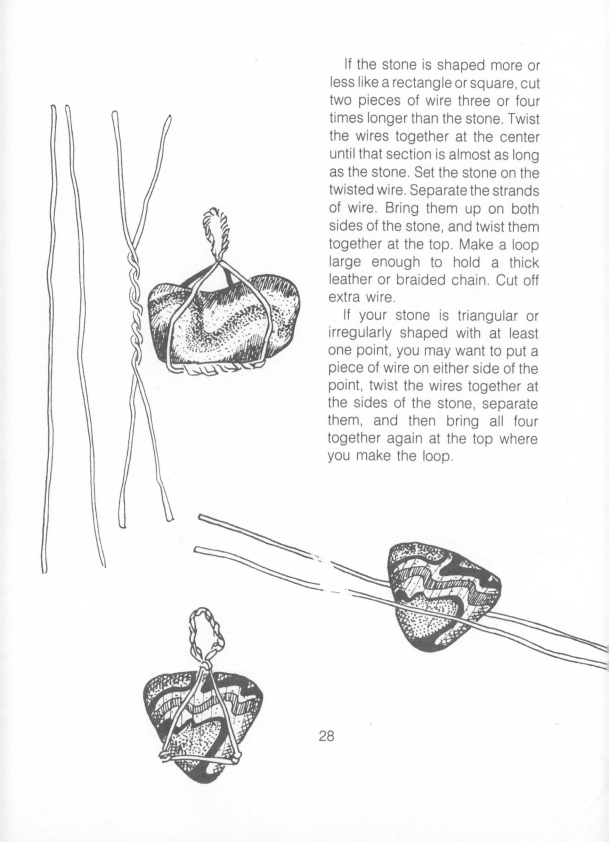

If the stone is shaped more or less like a rectangle or square, cut two pieces of wire three or four times longer than the stone. Twist the wires together at the center until that section is almost as long as the stone. Set the stone on the twisted wire. Separate the strands of wire. Bring them up on both sides of the stone, and twist them together at the top. Make a loop large enough to hold a thick leather or braided chain. Cut off extra wire.

If your stone is triangular or irregularly shaped with at least one point, you may want to put a piece of wire on either side of the point, twist the wires together at the sides of the stone, separate them, and then bring all four together again at the top where you make the loop.

28

Experiment. Design your own case to hold your amulet. For a chain, you can use a leather thong, bright-colored yarn, a braided rope made of different colors of crochet cotton, or a length of macrame.

*Variation: To make a painted stone amulet, choose a dull-colored stone and paint a design on it.*

### Macrame Chain

**Materials:** crochet thread
**Equipment:** safety pins; a large pillow or heavy cardboard

Some people think the art of macrame (knotting threads or yarns in special ways) originated in North Africa, was taken to Spain, then to Italy, and then to the rest of the world.

The work board for macrame can be any stiff surface into which you can put pins. It is easy to use a large pillow. A safety pin fastened near the top will hold the thread in place as you work.

Cut a length of crochet cotton about six times as long as you want your finished chain to be. Tie the thread onto the safety pin so that you have two lengths, one of which is at least twice as long as the other. Pull the shorter length down straight and pin it to the

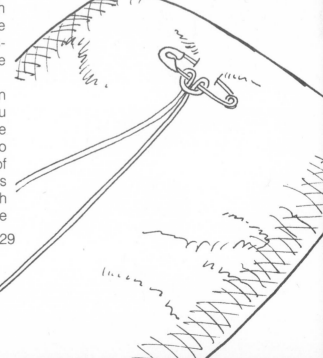

bottom of the pillow to keep it taut. If it extends beyond the pillow, don't worry—you can move your work up when part of the chain is completed.

Call the short length of cord A and the long one B. To make a knot, bring B down beside A, over A and under A, above where B crossed A. Then bring the end out between B and A. (See diagram) The aim is to continue to make knots, keeping them in an even line and all on the same side of the short thread. When the chain is as long as you want it, take the thread off the pillow. Make a knot at the end.

This chain may be used to hold the stone amulet.

# 3

## Bread for a
## Fighting Giant

Those who tell of the days of the Irish giants always mention two. Fin M'Coul, who lived at the very tip-top of Knockmany Hill, and Cucullin, who was beyond all doubt a thumper. No other giant of the day could stand before him. Such was his strength that, when really vexed, he would give a stamp that shook the country about him.

The fame and name of Cucullin went far and near, and nothing, it was said, in the shape of a man had any chance with him in a fight. He had given every giant in Ireland a thorough beating, barring Fin M'Coul himself, and he swore that he would never rest day or night, summer or winter, till he had served Fin with the same sauce—if he could catch him.

Now it happened that one day Fin was working on the Giant's Causeway, when he got word Cucullin was coming to have a trial of strength. This news gave Fin a sudden desire to see how his warm and affectionate wife Oonagh was getting along in his absence. So he pulled up a fir tree, lopped off the roots and branches, used the trunk as a walking stick, and set off toward his home on the top of Knockmany.

31

Now, many people wondered why Fin had chosen such a windy spot for his dwelling, and even went so far as to tease him for his reason. "What do you mean, Mr. M'Coul," they asked, "pitching your home on top of Knockmany, where there's a gale day and night, summer and winter, and where you are forced to wear your nightcap all the time. And then there's the want of water."

"Why," replied Fin, "ever since I was a lad, I've known that I'd like to have a house with a view. And where could I find a better spot for a view than on top of Knockmany? As for water, I'm sinking a well and, please goodness, when the Causeway's made, I'll finish it."

Now this was Fin's way of concealing the real reason for living upon the top of Knockmany. He really wanted to keep a sharp lookout to see Cucullin coming toward his house. He couldn't have found a more convenient situation in all Ireland.

"God save all here!" roared Fin, as he pushed his jolly face inside his own door.

"Fin! You are welcome home to your own Oonagh, my darling bully boy," cried his wife, giving him a great smacking kiss.

Fin spent three happy days with Oonagh and felt quite comfortable—considering the dread he had of Cucullin. But as time went by, he grew uneasy, and his wife saw that he had something on his mind that he was not talking about. But a wife has a way to wheedle something out of her good man, and Fin was proof of this.

"It's this Cucullin," he said, "that's troubling me. When

this fellow gets angry and begins to stamp, he shakes a whole town down."

As Fin spoke, he popped his thumb into his mouth, as he always did when he wanted to prophesy.

"What's that for?" asked his wife.

"He's coming," replied Fin. "I see him below Dungannon."

"And who is it you see?" asked Oonagh.

"That beast Cucullin," answered Fin, "and how to manage I don't know. If I run away, I am disgraced. Sooner or later I must meet him, for my thumb tells me so."

"When will he be here?" asked she.

"Tomorrow, about two o'clock," groaned Fin.

"Well, my dear, don't be cast down," said Oonagh. "Depend on me, and maybe I'll bring you out of this scare better than ever you could bring yourself out by the rule of your thumb."

She lit a fire on top of the hill, after which she put her finger to her mouth and gave three whistles. By doing this she let Cucullin know that he was invited to Knockmany, for in this way the Irish long ago gave a sign to strangers and travelers that they were welcome to come and share whatever was going on.

In the meantime, Fin was melancholy. He did not know what to do or how to act. Cucullin was an ugly opponent to meet. What chance did he have, strong and brave as he was, with a man who, when in a passion, could stamp the country into earthquakes? Fin did not know whether to go or stay. Even if he went, where could he go?

"Oonagh," he said in desperation, "can you do nothing

for me? Where is your invention? Am I to be skivered like a rabbit before your eyes and have my name disgraced forever in the sight of all my tribe—and me the best man among them? How am I to fight this man-mountain, this huge cross between earthquake and thunderbolt?"

"Be easy," soothed Oonagh. "Let him come, and do just as I bid you." This relieved Fin very much, for after all, he had great confidence in his wife, knowing as he did that she had got him out of many a scrape before.

Oonagh made the rounds of her neighbors and borrowed one and twenty frying pans. Then she baked one and twenty loaves of bread, putting a frying pan inside each one. After that, she baked some loaves without frying pans, being very careful to keep the two bakings separate.

The baking done, Oonagh set about making a huge baby dress, big enough for Fin, because Cucullin was expected the next day at two o'clock, as Fin knew by sucking his thumb. Now this was a curious property that Fin's thumb had—being able to tell Fin what was going to happen.

Next day, Cucullin was seen crossing the valley, and Oonagh knew it was time to carry out her plans. She fetched the cradle, giant size, and told Fin to put on the baby clothes, lie down in the cradle, and cover himself.

"You must pass yourself off for your own child," she instructed him. "Just lie there snug and say nothing. Leave it all to me."

About two o'clock, as expected, Cucullin came in.

"God save all here!" said he. "Is this where the great Fin M'Coul lives?"

"Indeed it is, honest man," answered Oonagh. "Won't you sit down?"

"Thank you, ma'm," said Cucullin, taking a seat. "You're Mrs. M'Coul, I suppose."

"I am," she replied, "and I have no reason, I hope, to be ashamed of my husband."

"No, indeed," said the guest. "He has the name of being the strongest and bravest man in Ireland. But for all that, there's a man not far from you who desires to take a shake with him. Is he at home?"

"Why, no," she answered, "and if ever a man left his house in a fury, he did. It appears that someone told him that a giant named Cucullin was down at the Causeway looking for him, and so he set off to catch the fellow. I hope for the poor giant's sake he won't meet with him; for if he does, Fin will make paste of him at once."

"Well," said the giant. "I am Cucullin, and I have been seeking Fin these twelve months—and I'll never rest day or night until I lay hands on him."

At this Oonagh gave a loud laugh of great contempt and looked at Cucullin as if he were a mere handful of a man.

"Did you ever see Fin?" she queried, changing her manner all at once.

"See him? How could I?" retorted the giant. "He always takes care to keep his distance."

"I thought so," nodded Oonagh, "and if you take my advice, you poor-looking creature, you'll pray night and day that you never see him. For I tell you, it will be a dark day for you if you do. In the meantime, you may notice that the wind is blowing in my door; as Fin himself is not at home, maybe you'd be civil enough to turn the house, as Fin always does when he's here."

This was a startler for Cucullin, but he got up, and after pulling the middle finger of his right hand until it cracked three times, he went outside, and putting his arms around the house, turned it as Oonagh wished.

When Fin in his cradle saw this, he felt sweat oozing out of every pore, but Oonagh was not daunted.

"Ah, then, as you are so civil, maybe you'd do another obliging thing for us, as Fin's not here to do it himself. You see, after the long stretch of dry weather we've been having, we're badly in need of water. Now Fin says there's

36

a fine spring-well somewhere under the rocks behind the hill below, and he intends to pull them apart. But as I told you, he went off in a rage, and I suppose he forgot. But if you'd try to find it, I'd feel obliged."

She took Cucullin down to see the place, which was one solid rock. After looking at it for some time, he cracked the middle finger of his right hand nine times, and stooping down, tore a cleft about four hundred feet deep and a quarter of a mile in length, which has since been called Lumbord's Glen.

"Won't you come in now," invited Oonagh, "and eat a bit of our humble fare? Even though you and Fin are enemies, he would want you treated kindly in our house. Indeed, if I didn't look after you in his absence, he'd be displeased with me."

She took the giant in, and placing him at the table, she put before him a half dozen of the first loaves she had baked with the frying pans inside, two pounds of butter, a side of boiled bacon, and a stack of cabbage. Then she begged him to eat.

Cucullin put one of the loaves of bread in his mouth, took a huge bite of it, and made a thundering noise—something between a growl and a yell.

"Sound and fury!" he shouted. "What's this? Two of my teeth are out. What kind of bread did you give me?"

"What's the matter with it?" Oonagh asked coolly.

"Matter!" yelled Cucullin. "Why the two best teeth in my head are gone!"

"Why," said Oonagh, opening her eyes in wide surprise. "That's Fin's bread—the only bread he ever eats when he's at home! But I must tell you that only he and that child in the cradle there can eat it. I thought a rather stout fellow like yourself might be able to manage. Here's another cake. Maybe it's not as hard as the first."

By this time Cucullin was not only hungry, but ravenous. He made a fresh start with the second loaf, and at once gave a yell twice as loud as the first.

"Thunder and gibbets!" he roared. "Take your bread away! I won't have a tooth left in my head. Another pair of them gone!"

"Honest man," said Oonagh, "if you don't want to eat the bread, say so quietly, and don't wake the child in the cradle. Oh, now you've wakened him!"

Fin let out a shriek that startled Cucullin, coming from a babe as young as Fin was supposed to be.

"Now, now," said Oonagh. "I know you are hungry, my little one." She handed him a loaf of bread that had no frying pan in it. Fin, whose appetite had been sharpened by all the eating going on, grabbed it, chewed, and swallowed.

Cucullin, watching carefully, was thunderstruck. He thanked his stars that he had had the good fortune to miss Fin, for as he said to himself, "I'd have no chance with a man who can eat bread such as that. Even his son, who is in the cradle, eats bread that knocks my teeth out."

"I'd like a glimpse of that lad in the cradle," said he to Oonagh, "for I'm sure that a child who can manage your bread is no joke to look at."

"Look at him, then," said Oonagh, drawing back the covers, showing off her darling Fin dressed as a baby.

"He's the image of his father, who was also this big when a babe."

When Cucullin saw the giant babe lying there in the cradle, he began to think what size the father might be, and his knees knocked together with fright. So he made haste to bid Oonagh farewell and to assure her that, from that day on, he never wished to hear, much less see, her husband.

"I admit I'm not much of a match for him—strong as I am. Tell him I'll avoid him and make myself scarce in this part of the country."

With these words, Cucullin rushed out of the house.

"It's well for you that Fin isn't here," called Oonagh as she watched the fleeting giant. "Fin would have made hawks' meat out of you!"

Thus did Oonagh, through wit and invention, overcome an enemy who never could have been beaten by force.

*(An Irish tale)*

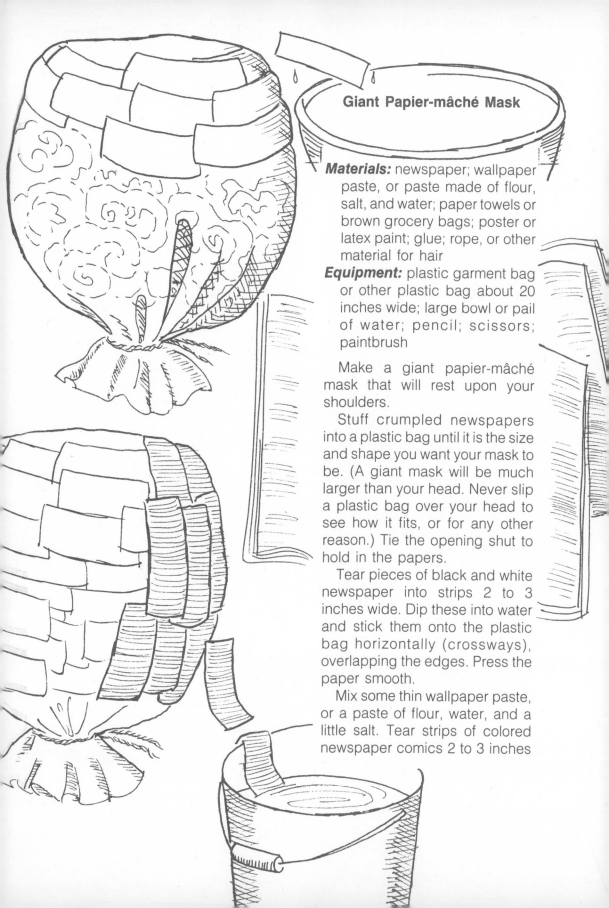

## Giant Papier-mâché Mask

**Materials:** newspaper; wallpaper paste, or paste made of flour, salt, and water; paper towels or brown grocery bags; poster or latex paint; glue; rope, or other material for hair

**Equipment:** plastic garment bag or other plastic bag about 20 inches wide; large bowl or pail of water; pencil; scissors; paintbrush

Make a giant papier-mâché mask that will rest upon your shoulders.

Stuff crumpled newspapers into a plastic bag until it is the size and shape you want your mask to be. (A giant mask will be much larger than your head. Never slip a plastic bag over your head to see how it fits, or for any other reason.) Tie the opening shut to hold in the papers.

Tear pieces of black and white newspaper into strips 2 to 3 inches wide. Dip these into water and stick them onto the plastic bag horizontally (crossways), overlapping the edges. Press the paper smooth.

Mix some thin wallpaper paste, or a paste of flour, water, and a little salt. Tear strips of colored newspaper comics 2 to 3 inches wide. Dip strips into paste. Stick them onto the stuffed plastic bag vertically (up and down), over-lapping the edges. If small areas of the black and white paper still show, tear bits of paper and paste on, making the surface smooth.

For the third layer, use black and white newspaper strips. Dip these into the paste and com-pletely cover the colored strips, going around and around the mask diagonally.

For the fourth and final layer, use either paper toweling or brown grocery bags torn into 2- to 3-inch strips.

Set the mask aside for several days to let it dry thoroughly.

When the mask is dry, remove the plastic bag with the news-paper stuffing. If the opening is not large enough to allow you to slip the mask over your head, carefully cut away some of the papier-mâché. Now try on the mask. Ask someone to mark the position of your eyes with a pencil. Take off the mask and draw a face with an opening for your eyes in the place marked. That opening can be the mouth of the mask. Cut that place out.

Draw a pattern for ears, allow-ing for an inch tab at the straight side. Cut out four ears, using brown paper. With wallpaper paste, fasten two ears together to

make one, leaving the tabs un-pasted. Shape the ears while the paper is wet. Separate the tabs on each ear and paste them in place on the mask. Paste additional paper over the tabs to hold the ears firmly in place.

Make a cone of brown paper. Trim the open edge into the shape of a nose. Glue the back of the cone onto the mask. Reinforce with strips of paper until the nose is held firmly in place.

If you want your giant to have bushy eyebrows, dip strips of paper into the paste. Crumple them into wads and shape them like eyebrows. Press them in place on the mask. Cover with small strips of paste-covered paper to hold them in place. Set aside to dry.

When the mask is dry, paint it with an overall coat of poster or latex paint. After this is dry, paint the features. For hair, you can glue on rope, paper, or any other kind of hair you can imagine.

### Cut-paper Designs

**Materials:** paper, white or colored
**Equipment:** scissors; pencil

Ireland always has been a land of contrasts. While some people in olden times were telling stories

42

about ugly fighting giants, other people were producing beautiful artwork, using a great variety of materials, ranging from precious metals and jewels, to paper.

Some authorities claim the Celts (the early Irish) and Anglo-Saxons (the early English) originated the art of making cut-paper designs. Regardless of who first developed the art, the Celts and Anglo-Saxons did produce, as early as the seventh century, Gospel books with cut-paper decorations on some pages.

Perhaps you have made snowflake designs by folding paper and cutting at random along the fold. You can also make more carefully planned designs to resemble Irish cut-paper art.

In cut-paper art, it is easiest to start with a single-fold design. Fold the paper in half. Draw shapes along the fold, making sure that large sections of uncut paper will remain. Draw the design also on the outer edges. Cut out the design. Open the paper. Notice how the design is duplicated.

To make another type, fold the paper in half from top to bottom, and then from side to side. Draw a design. It will be repeated four times after the paper has been cut and opened.

Or work with triangles. Fold a

square of paper in half diagonally, so that it forms a triangle. Fold that triangle in half to form a smaller one. Draw a design near the folded tip of the triangle and along the folded edges. Remember you must leave some uncut sections along the fold, and other uncut sections to hold the design together. Cut out the design. Open the paper, and see the design.

No matter what shape paper you use, or how many times you fold it, you must take certain steps in order to get a clear-cut design.

1. Fold the sheet of paper so the edges are even.
2. Crease each fold well.
3. Draw a design that can be duplicated when the paper is opened. Remember to cut only here and there along a fold.
4. When you are ready to cut, grasp the paper firmly or use paper clips, so the layers will not slip.
5. Hold the scissors more or less in one position, moving the paper, rather than the scissors, as you cut.

Try folding paper of different sizes and shapes and drawing and cutting designs, to see what interesting patterns you can make. If the work interests you, study art books and make more complicated designs.

44

## Eighteenth Century Greeting Cards

*Additional material:* paint

To make an old-fashioned greeting card, fold a piece of paper in quarters. Draw a design along the outer edges. Leave the center section in one piece so you can write a message there. After you cut out your design, paint flowers, hearts, or designs around the outer edges, as people did when this type handmade card was popular.

## Mounted and Painted Designs

*Additional Materials:* paste; paint; felt-tip pen

Fold a sheet of paper, either white or colored. Draw a design and cut it out. Open the paper. Paste the design on a sheet of white paper the same size. Paint each section of the bottom paper revealed through the cutout design. When the paint is dry, outline the design with a felt-tip pen.

# 4

## *The Biggest Fool*

Long ago, White Rabbit lived near the ocean on the island of Japan. He longed to travel, but how far can a rabbit go, when all he can do is hop around on an island?

Standing on his long legs, which gave him extra height, White Rabbit could see a land far across the ocean. He wanted to cross the water and visit the strange land. But how? He couldn't swim like a fish, or fly like a bird. He had no boat, and besides, he was no sailor.

White Rabbit sat down on the beach and thought and thought, trying to discover a way to cross the ocean. And as he sat there, along came King Shark.

"Good day, Mr. White Rabbit," said King Shark politely.

"Good day to you," answered White Rabbit.

"What are you doing?" asked King Shark.

"I've been wondering," said White Rabbit, thinking fast, "how many of you sharks live in the ocean?"

"Well, I don't know," answered King Shark, for in truth, he didn't know.

"Wouldn't you like to know?" asked White Rabbit.

"Oh, yes!" said King Shark.

"I'll tell you what we can do," continued White Rabbit. "I know how to count."

King Shark marveled at this ability.

"Get all the sharks to come here to be counted," suggested White Rabbit. "Ask them to line up single file, nose to fin, starting from where you are now, straight to the shore over there." He pointed to the land he wanted to visit. "I'll jump from shark to shark, one by one, and count you—if you want me to."

"Oh, yes, I want you to," said King Shark and off he swam.

In no time at all, the word was spread. All the sharks in the ocean came to the island of Japan and got in line, single file, nose to fin, and so they formed a bridge between Japan and the land across the ocean.

"Oh, you wonderful, wonderful sharks!" exclaimed White Rabbit. "Now, help me count. Repeat after me in unison, "one, two, three."

The sharks did so.

"Now count with me. Ready, everyone!"

Screaming the first number, "Onnnnnnnnne," White Rabbit jumped from the beach onto the back of the first shark. Then he continued to jump from shark to shark, counting:

> . . . two—three—
> four—five—six—
> seven—eight—nine—
> Tennnnnnnnnn!

One—two—three—
four—five—six—
seven—eight—nine—
Tennnnnnnnnn!

White Rabbit jumped along, counting the sharks, one by one, repeating the numbers one through ten, over and over again, never bothering to keep track of how many times he had counted one through ten, until finally he landed on the back of the last shark, King Shark.

There White Rabbit stopped to look back at the sharks. He could keep the joke to himself no longer. He burst out laughing.

"You fools!" he cried. "You think I wanted to count sharks? I wanted to cross the ocean to visit a new land.

The sharks in the ocean are one-through-ten fools, over and over again!"

Angered by these words, King Shark lurched, so that as White Rabbit jumped, he landed not on the land, but in the sea. King Shark scooped him up and tossed him back to the shark behind him, who tossed him to the shark behind him, who tossed him to the shark behind him, one through ten times, over and over again.

At last, White Rabbit landed right back where he had started, badly shaken, bruised, and very unhappy.

Mikoto, Prince and Lord of the Big Island, passed by and saw poor White Rabbit, lying on the beach, panting.

"What happened?" asked the prince.

In tears, White Rabbit told how he had cleverly outwitted the sharks, only to have them make a fool of him.

"It seems to me," said the prince, "that you were a little slow in finding out what most creatures know. The biggest fool is the one who tries to make a fool of someone else."

"I know it now," sighed White Rabbit.

"Then," instructed the prince, "go wash yourself in the fresh water of the river. Make a bed of cattail down. Lie down, and rest awhile. You will recover, and perhaps someday you will become a truly clever and quick-witted rabbit."

*(A Japanese tale retold)*

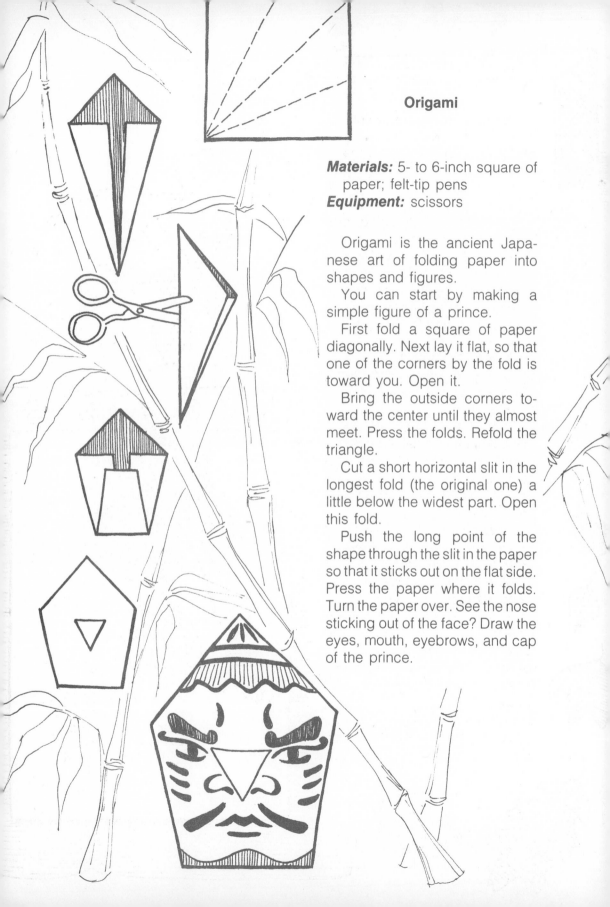

## Origami

**Materials:** 5- to 6-inch square of paper; felt-tip pens
**Equipment:** scissors

Origami is the ancient Japanese art of folding paper into shapes and figures.

You can start by making a simple figure of a prince.

First fold a square of paper diagonally. Next lay it flat, so that one of the corners by the fold is toward you. Open it.

Bring the outside corners toward the center until they almost meet. Press the folds. Refold the triangle.

Cut a short horizontal slit in the longest fold (the original one) a little below the widest part. Open this fold.

Push the long point of the shape through the slit in the paper so that it sticks out on the flat side. Press the paper where it folds. Turn the paper over. See the nose sticking out of the face? Draw the eyes, mouth, eyebrows, and cap of the prince.

## Scroll
## (of imitation parchment)

**Materials:** Two straight twigs or ¼-inch dowels; freezer-wrap paper; facial tissue; small leaves; household or school glue; water; pretty string, crochet cotton, or cord

**Equipment:** newspaper; paintbrush ½- to 1-inch wide; scissors; ruler; pencil; teaspoon for measuring; small clean tin can or dish to hold diluted glue

Flowers and plants are often used in Japanese art. This parchment-like scroll gives a feeling of the Orient.

Collect a number of small leaves that will lie flat. If possible, choose different shapes and colors in order to create variety in design. Cut off stems unless they are very thin.

Separate one sheet of facial tissue so that you have a single layer. Cut a piece of freezer wrap as wide as the facial tissue and 2 inches longer.

Place newspaper on your workspace. Lay the freezer wrap wax side down. Arrange the leaves on the paper in a design, leaving 1-inch margin top and bottom. Do not overlap leaves. Cut off any stems that stick up.

Glue the leaves onto the paper.

51

Press each leaf so that all parts are flat. If glue oozes out, never mind.

Measure a teaspoon of glue and put it in a small can or dish. Add an equal amount of water. One teaspoon of glue and one of water is enough to make one scroll.

Using a wide paintbrush, spread diluted glue over the leaves and then over the paper.

Lay the single thickness of facial tissue over the leaves so the sides are even, and about an inch of freezer wrap extends at the top and bottom. Gently pat down the tissue over the leaves.

Fill your paintbrush with as much diluted glue as it will hold. Paint gently over the facial tissue, making sure that every spot is very wet, at the same time being careful not to tear it. The facial tissue will wrinkle a little. This is all right. When dry, it will make the paper look like parchment.

Let the glue dry overnight.

Cut 2 straight twigs or ¼-inch dowels, 2 inches longer than the paper is wide. Twigs, if you can find them without hurting a tree, are prettier than dowels.

Turn the leaf design upside down on the workspace. Put undiluted glue on the part of the paper that extends below the facial tissue. Wrap the paper around a twig or dowel, with the stick on the back of the scroll. Hold the roll tight until the stick is glued in place. Glue a stick on top of the scroll in the same way.

Cut a piece of crochet cotton, pretty string, or cord, 1 inch longer than the scroll is wide. Tie one end around the stick on each side of the top of the scroll, for hanging.

*Variation: Dry and press small flowers by placing them between sheets of paper toweling or similar paper and putting a weight on top. When the flowers are dry and flat, use them to make a design for a scroll.*

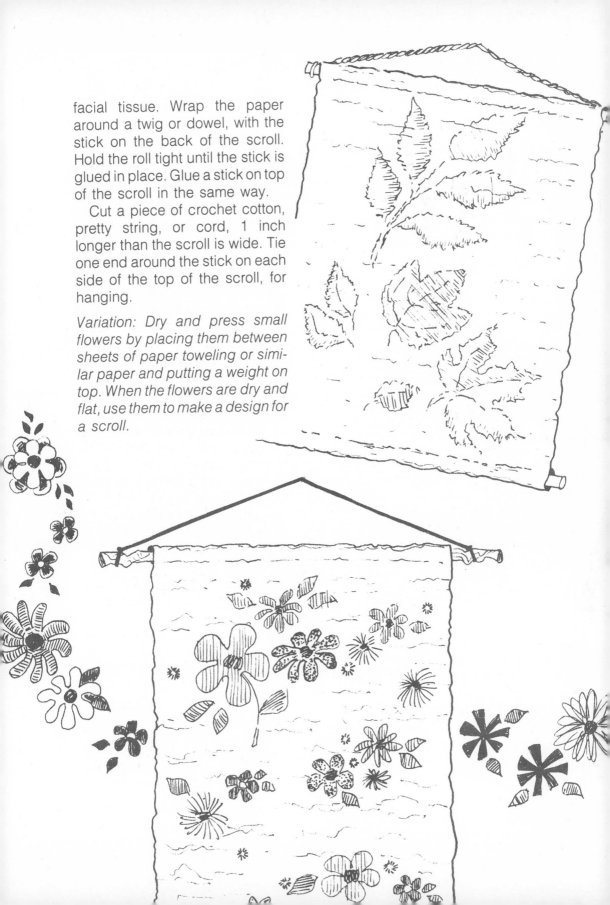

# 5

## *The Fisherman and the Genie*

A fisherman who lived near the Mediterranean Sea prospered, when he was a young man. The fish were plentiful, the market good, and after he had made his sales, he always had enough left to feed his family. Part of his success lay in the fact that he never took more fish than he could sell or use before they spoiled. "I'll always leave fish in the sea to spawn and produce more fish," he said.

As the years passed, in spite of his precautions, he caught fewer and fewer fish, and he took more and more rubble from the bottom of the sea: broken pottery, remains of old ships, and all manner of sea creatures impossible to sell for food.

Yet, discouraged as he was, the fisherman continued to cast his net in the same spot, trusting that each new day might bring better luck than the one before it.

One morning, the fisherman cast his net as usual. When it was heavy, he pulled it up and discovered the skeleton of a donkey. "Woe is me!" he cried as he disentangled the bones of the donkey and mended his net. "I have no flocks, no herds, no vineyards. I depend upon my catch of fish to feed my wife and children. And what do I catch? Donkey bones!"

The fisherman cast his net again. Soon it was heavy. With some effort, he pulled it up only to find it filled with broken bottles and pottery.

"Pity me!" cried the fisherman as he threw the broken bottles and pottery back into the sea. "I have no skill but fishing. Can I provide for my family with broken bottles and pottery?"

The fisherman cast his net a third time. This time, as he pulled in his catch, he noticed a dull urn. It was of copper, very old, and badly tarnished.

The fisherman rowed to the shore, where he brushed away the embedded sand and examined the urn more intently. "The seal is Solomon's!" he exclaimed. "The great King Solomon!  What treasure is in this urn?"

With great difficulty, he pried off the seal and pulled out the lead stopper. He looked into the urn and discovered—nothing! The urn was empty. Or so it seemed, until a great puff of smoke suddenly emerged and ascended like a pillar of mist, turning from gray to green to purple, growing greater and greater.

The mist spread out, but it did not disappear, as smoke from a chimney often does. It began to take shape. Some wisps became arms; a ball became an oval and then a head. More misty smoke became a twisting floating body, getting thinner, fatter, thinner, forever changing shape.

Suddenly, the shape swooped down and placed its forehead at the feet of the fisherman. "Great King Solomon! Good King Solomon!" it cried. "Now that you

55

have released me, forgive me, your disobedient servant. Never more will I oppose your will. Honor my one request. Grant pardon."

The fisherman was dumbfounded. At last he spoke. "What are you talking about, great spirit, genie, whatever you may be? King Solomon has been dead eighteen hundred years."

"Are you not the great King Solomon?" asked the genie, for such he was, his green eyes flashing through the smoke. "Are you not King Solomon?"

"No, spirit, I am a fisherman," came the answer.

"A fisherman!" screamed the genie. "If you are not the great King Solomon, I must kill you."

"Kill me? Why?" asked the fisherman." I released you from an urn. Why kill me?"

"Because I have taken a vow," replied the genie.

"A vow? Please explain before you kill me," begged the fisherman in a calm voice. "Surely a great spirit like you, a genie who knew the wise King Solomon, must offer some explanation before he kills a humble man and thereby makes his children fatherless, and his wife a widow without a provider. In the name of the great King Solomon, tell me about your oath, proud spirit."

"Proud spirit! You call me a proud spirit?" screamed the genie.

The fisherman stood silent, looking at the genie steadfastly.

"Proud spirit," repeated the genie humbly. "Yes, fisherman, you are right. It was my proud spirit that caused my downfall. I alone, of all the genies, refused to humble myself before the great King Solomon and declare allegiance to him. Whereupon, he captured me and sealed me in the urn that you have found."

"But your vow?" the fisherman asked.

"Oh, yes," continued the genie, "during the first hundred years of my captivity, I vowed I would make anyone who set me free a rich person. Unless, of course, King Solomon released me. I could not reward him.

"During the second hundred years of captivity, I vowed that I would open up all the treasures of the earth and give them to the person who set me free.

"During the third hundred years, I vowed that I would make my deliverer a wealthy prince and serve him always. As the centuries went by, I added more and more promises. Then I grew weary. I realized that good wishes

57

would never bring my release. I nullified all my former vows and made a new oath.

"I vowed I would kill the person who opened the urn and set me free, unless that person were King Solomon himself. In this way I would punish all the people who had failed, over the centuries, to release me. You opened the urn. You set me free. So I must kill you!"

"I understand," said the fisherman, not understanding at all, but knowing full well that the genie was in no mood to reason.

"I know that a vow is a vow. It must be kept," the fisherman continued. "If a genie makes a vow, he must keep it. So you must keep your vow, if—," he added slowly, "if you are indeed a genie, a genie who was in that urn."

"If I am a genie?" screamed the spirit. "What makes you doubt that I am a genie? What makes you doubt I was in that urn?"

"Because," explained the fisherman, speaking slowly and staring at the genie, "as I see you now, you are very large, towering into the sky. How can so large a spirit fit into an urn that size?"

"Because I am a genie. I can turn into anything."

"Then, great genie, before I die, I ask you to grant my one request, as you begged the great King Solomon to grant yours."

"In the name of the great King Solomon, I grant you one request."

"Show me you are the genie who was in that urn. Return

to the urn," begged the fisherman, "so that I may die knowing that you have not lied to me."

"As you wish," said the genie. "A foolish fisherman needs proof."

With a swoosh of air, the genie reduced his size and gushed into the urn. In a second the fisherman replaced the lead stopper and pounded it in.

"Let me go! Let me go!" screamed the genie.

"Never! Never!" replied the fisherman. "I now take a vow. I will never let you go."

"I'll change myself into a lion and devour you!" threatened the genie as he roared like a lion and clawed the urn.

"Never!" said the fisherman as he pounded on the stopper.

"Let me go, or I'll change myself into all the demons of hell and earth, and haunt you forever!" The genie let out sounds so wild and eerie that birds flew out of the trees, and animals ran away from the fields that edged the beach.

"Threats and wild screams will not open this urn," said the fisherman.

The genie changed his methods then: "Oh, good kind fisherman, do open the urn. If you let me go, I will make you rich forever and ever. Your family will be cared for. I vow! I vow!"

"If I let you go, you will remain a wicked genie forever and ever. I, too, have taken a vow. I will never let you go!"

With these words, the fisherman tied a rock around the neck of the urn, got into his boat, and rowed far out into the

Mediterranean Sea, where the water was deepest. There he dumped overboard the ancient urn with the genie trapped inside.

The fisherman started to row to shore, stopped, and lowered his net in the deep water. Soon, very soon, it was filled with fish.

"Strange," mused the fisherman as he looked at his catch. "Strange. With no intent on his part, the wicked genie helped me find a better place to fish."

*(A tale retold from Arabian Nights)*

## Wet-chalk Genie

**Materials:** colored chalk; water; typing paper or heavy drawing paper; construction paper; paste

**Equipment:** sponge; newspaper; scissors; bath towel; iron

A wet-chalk drawing can have the appearance of a genie floating on high above the urn from which he came.

Cover the workspace with newspapers. Using a wet sponge, dampen a piece of white paper well.

Break colored chalk into pieces no more than 1 inch long. With a piece of chalk, draw the head of a genie near the top of the wet paper. Take another color chalk. Hold it sideways, and make sweeping strokes for the arms, body, and legs of the genie. Add other colors if you wish.

You may want to make two or three pictures of genies, with arms and legs in different positions, and later choose which one you'd like for the final picture.

Let the paper dry.

Draw and cut out of construction paper a bottle or urn that might have held the genie.

Choose your favorite genie painting. You will find that in drying, the paper has curled up.

To iron it flat, place it face down on a bath towel, and set the regulator on the iron to warm or wool temperature. Iron the paper gently.

Paste the construction paper urn on the picture.

## Swirl Painting
### (oil on water)

**Materials:** heavy paper that won't go to pieces when dipped in water; oil paint (model paint works well)

**Equipment:** shallow pan; petroleum jelly; piece of heavy wire; newspaper; inexpensive rubber gloves, or the disposable plastic kind

Swirl painting can look like the surface of a glimmering sea.

To make the cleanup job easier, coat the inside of a shallow pan with petroleum jelly. Wear a smock or heavy apron, and gloves.

Cover your workspace and the place where you plan to let your paintings dry with several layers of newspaper. Pour some water into the shallow pan you have greased. Dribble one color of oil paint slowly on the water, here and there. Add drops of another color.

Swirl the drops of paint around

62

with the tip of a wire. You can see interesting designs forming and you'll note that oil paint and water do not mix.

Holding a sheet of heavy paper with both hands, dip it and slide it slowly under the paint. Let it remain a moment until the water is still. Slowly lift the paper, letting swirls of oil collect on it and stick to it. Allow the water to drain slowly off the paper.

Place the painting on several thicknesses of newspaper, and let it dry.

Stir the water and paint with the wire. Add more paint if necessary. Make another design. Each design will be different.

### Undersea Watercolor
### (with tape resist)

**Materials:** watercolor paints; water; heavy-weight typing paper; masking tape; scrap paper; construction paper; paste; felt-tip pens, if desired

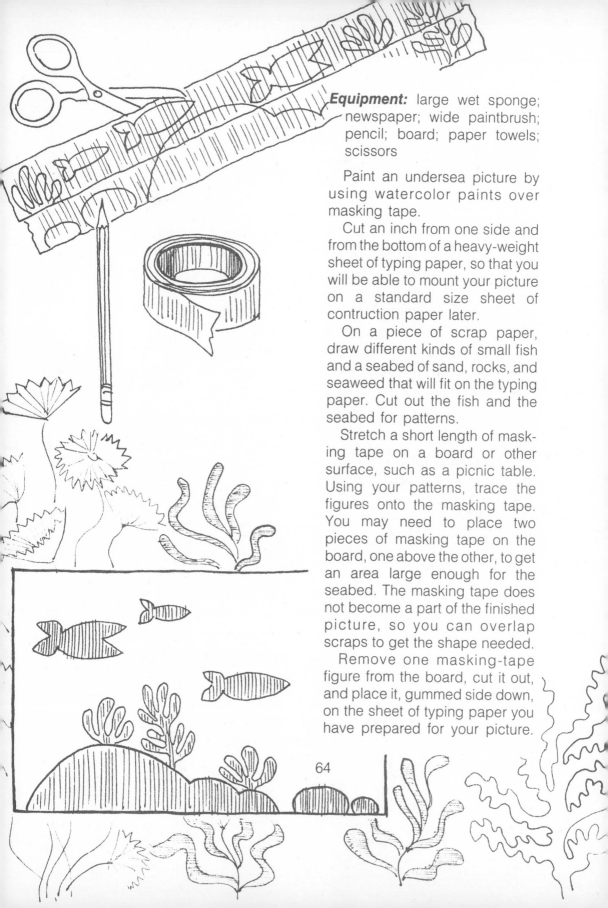

**Equipment:** large wet sponge; newspaper; wide paintbrush; pencil; board; paper towels; scissors

Paint an undersea picture by using watercolor paints over masking tape.

Cut an inch from one side and from the bottom of a heavy-weight sheet of typing paper, so that you will be able to mount your picture on a standard size sheet of contruction paper later.

On a piece of scrap paper, draw different kinds of small fish and a seabed of sand, rocks, and seaweed that will fit on the typing paper. Cut out the fish and the seabed for patterns.

Stretch a short length of masking tape on a board or other surface, such as a picnic table. Using your patterns, trace the figures onto the masking tape. You may need to place two pieces of masking tape on the board, one above the other, to get an area large enough for the seabed. The masking tape does not become a part of the finished picture, so you can overlap scraps to get the shape needed.

Remove one masking-tape figure from the board, cut it out, and place it, gummed side down, on the sheet of typing paper you have prepared for your picture.

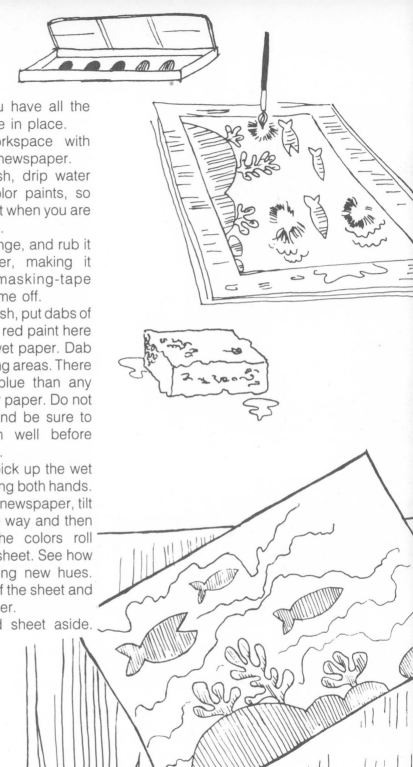

Continue, until you have all the parts of the picture in place.

Cover your workspace with several sheets of newspaper.

Using your brush, drip water onto your watercolor paints, so that they will be soft when you are ready to use them.

Wet a large sponge, and rub it across your paper, making it really wet. The masking-tape figures will not come off.

Using a wide brush, put dabs of green, yellow, and red paint here and there on the wet paper. Dab blue on all remaining areas. There should be more blue than any other color on your paper. Do not brush the paint, and be sure to clean your brush well before using a new color.

Now, carefully pick up the wet sheet of paper, using both hands. Holding it over the newspaper, tilt the wet paper one way and then another, letting the colors roll slowly across the sheet. See how they mingle, making new hues. Let the color run off the sheet and onto the newspaper.

Set the colored sheet aside.

When it is really dry, carefully remove the masking-tape figures. See the scene with white fish swimming above a white seabed.

You can leave the scene as it is, or you can add a few strokes with felt-tip pens, giving eyes and stripes to the fish, and shape to the rocks and seaweed.

Paste your undersea picture on a sheet of construction paper, leaving a margin.

# 6

## *The Burro's Load*

Pedro was a special kind of merchant. He bought things to sell and hauled them to his customers. But he did not own a cart. He had no need for one. The roads he had to travel were too rough, and the streams he had to cross were too many. A cart would have been bumped to pieces before he had rounded the first curve in the road.

Pedro depended upon his burro to carry the goods he had to sell. He would put all that he was expected to deliver into two bags, divide the weight evenly, tie the bags together with a stout rope, and then sling them across the back of the burro, so that a bundle dangled from each side.

A special kinship developed between Pedro and his burro. Pedro loved his burro and depended upon him to help earn a living. And in his way, the burro showed affection for Pedro, because he sensed that food and shelter came from his master.

But at times, the burro made it quite clear that he hated to carry loads, especially heavy ones, like salt. And Pedro hated to scold the animal, but when the burro was very stubborn, Pedro would pull one of its ears, and say, "I ought to beat you, as most masters do. But I won't. But why can't you understand, little burro? You have to help me haul the goods to make a living—a living for me and my family, and for you, too.

"And we'd like to have a little extra money, little burro, to buy something special for festival times. You like to wear bright bells and ribbons at a fiesta, and you like extra bundles of sweet hay. My children like piñatas and sweets for a feast day. Come, little burro, pull the load."

Then he would give the burro a whack, ever so gently, on his rump, and the two would go on.

Now, it happened that one hot day when the burro was carrying salt, it stopped in the middle of a stream. "Cool your feet, little burro," said Pedro. "I'm sure you are hot, and I see berries that I'd like to have, growing along the bank." He called, as he waded to shore, "Just a minute, and we'll be on our way again."

Or so Pedro thought. What a mistake! As soon as he turned his back to pick berries, the little burro lay down in the water.

Pedro turned and shouted from the bank. The burro stood up. How light his load was!

Pedro ran to the burro and jerked his rope. "Come on! Come on!" he yelled. "My salt has dissolved, or most of it, and gone downstream."

On they went, until they came to a second stream. This time Pedro stayed by the side of his burro, but that didn't help. Down into the stream the burro went again, and stayed there until all the salt had dissolved, and the bags were empty.

"What shall I do with you?" screamed Pedro. "I don't want to beat you. But you are useless, if you won't carry salt. I can't afford two burros—you to play at home and another to carry goods. How can I teach you a lesson?"

Pedro found a rock and sat down, still holding onto the burro's rope. He thought, "What can he carry that won't be harmed by water? How can I teach him a lesson?" Then an idea came to him.

Pedro led his burro to a seashore market, where he bought sponges, put them in bags, and tied the bundles on the burro's back. The load was light, and the burro jogged briskly along the road.

When they came to the stream, the burro sat down, just as Pedro had expected him to do. But when the burro stood up, the load was heavy, much to the burro's

surprise. The sponges had not dissolved, as the salt had done. Instead, they had soaked up the water, and the burro had to carry a burden of water-filled sponges.

Pedro led his burro home. It was a hard trip. They had to go slowly, for the load was heavy, and the water dripping from the sponges made the burro uncomfortable.

From that day on, Pedro had no problem with the burro when they crossed a stream.

*(A Mexican tale retold)*

## Paper-bag Burro Piñata

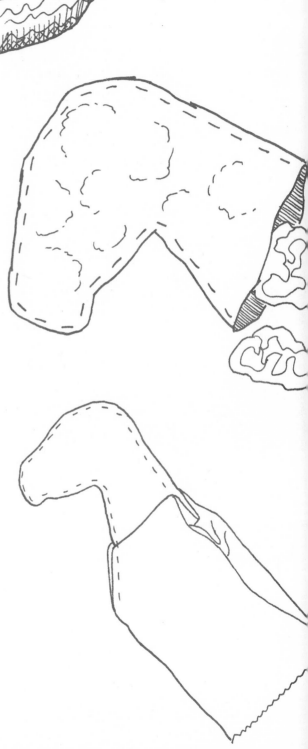

**Materials:** medium-sized heavy paper bag; more brown paper; newspaper; staples; 2-prong brass paper fasteners; masking tape; twine; paints or other materials for decorations; wrapped candy

**Equipment:** pencil; scissors; stapler; broomstick; short stout stick; rope; blindfold

A piñata is a decorated container filled with goodies. Modern piñatas, used during the Christmas season in Mexico, are usually made of papier-mâché. Paper-bag figures also serve well for family or group parties.

To make a burro piñata, use a medium-sized brown bag for the body. The head will be fastened on the bottom of the bag; the sides of the burro will be the sides of the bag; and the tail will be where the bag closes.

On brown paper, draw 2 identical profiles of a burro's head, with an elongated neck. Cut them out, and staple them together around the edges, leaving the neck open. Tear newspaper into small strips, and stuff the head of the burro.

Cut a slit in the bottom of the bag, and insert the head. Staple it in place. Tuck in the corner of the

71

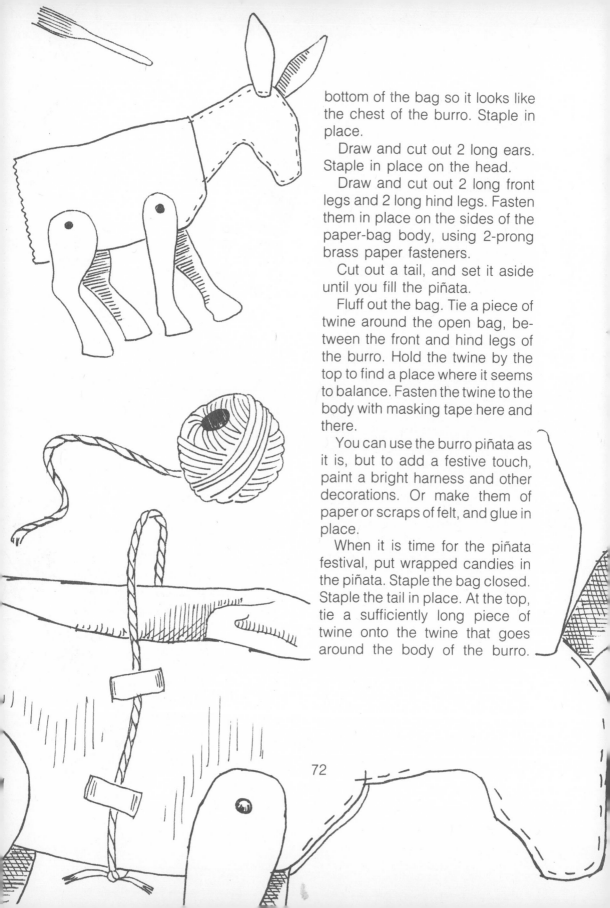

bottom of the bag so it looks like the chest of the burro. Staple in place.

Draw and cut out 2 long ears. Staple in place on the head.

Draw and cut out 2 long front legs and 2 long hind legs. Fasten them in place on the sides of the paper-bag body, using 2-prong brass paper fasteners.

Cut out a tail, and set it aside until you fill the piñata.

Fluff out the bag. Tie a piece of twine around the open bag, between the front and hind legs of the burro. Hold the twine by the top to find a place where it seems to balance. Fasten the twine to the body with masking tape here and there.

You can use the burro piñata as it is, but to add a festive touch, paint a bright harness and other decorations. Or make them of paper or scraps of felt, and glue in place.

When it is time for the piñata festival, put wrapped candies in the piñata. Staple the bag closed. Staple the tail in place. At the top, tie a sufficiently long piece of twine onto the twine that goes around the body of the burro.

72

Adjust the goodies in the bag so that the figure hangs fairly evenly.

In its traditional setting, the piñata is suspended by a rope from a balcony, where someone can raise or lower it. In the United States, it is often suspended from the end of a broomstick, held by a tall person standing on a chair.

To play the game, one player is blindfolded and given a stout stick. He is led to a spot below the suspended piñata. Everyone else stands a safe distance away. At a signal, the operator lowers the piñata, trying to make it swing a little. The blindfolded player tries to hit it with his stick, using enough force to break the container and cause the goodies to fall on the floor. Everyone then scrambles for the goodies. If the first player cannot break the piñata, another player is chosen.

*Note:* Excellent directions for making papier-mâché piñatas are given in *Piñatas* by Virginia Brock, Abingdon, 1966.

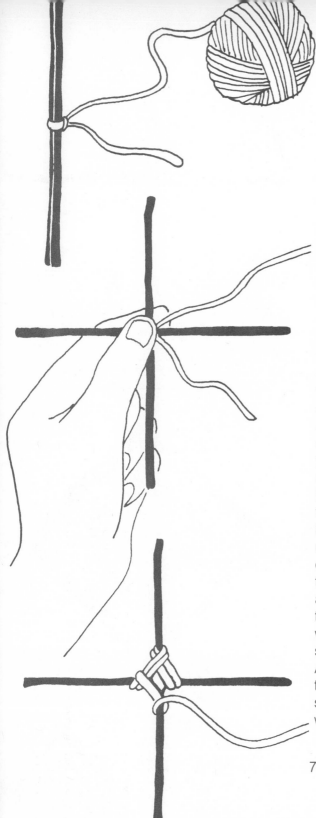

## Eye-of-God Weaving

**Materials:** yarn of related but different colors; twigs

**Equipment:** toothpick; scissors

Eye-of-God weaving is a Mexican art produced by winding brightly colored yarns around two sticks placed at right angles. There's a brightly colored design in the center (the eye of God), surrounded by bands of related colors.

Choose two straight twigs of equal length. Lay them in front of you. Unroll an arm's length of the color yarn you have chosen for the center of the design but do not cut it off. With it, tie a knot tightly around the center of the two sticks, leaving several inches of yarn on the loose end. Twist the sticks so that they form a cross. Hold the sticks at this angle with the thumb and forefinger of one hand. With the other hand, pick up the two strands of yarn, the one connected to the skein and the loose end. Wrap the strands around the stick nearest the knot, then cross to the next stick, and wrap the yarn over and under that stick. Then move to the third stick. Always weave in the same direction. Adjust your hold on the sticks so that the stick on which you are working is closest to you.

When you have used up the

74

short end of yarn, continue to weave with one strand.

When you want to change colors, cut the yarn, leaving a loose end. Tuck this up under the woven yarn at the back of the design. A toothpick may be helpful. Insert the new yarn under the same place at the back.

Continue to weave and change colors until the design is complete. Do not weave all the way to the ends of the twigs. They are part of the design.

*Note:* Beginners may find it easier to work with flat sticks, such as popsicle sticks or tongue depressors. Glue the sticks together at right angles and let the glue set. To start, the end of the yarn may be glued onto the stick. If you have trouble tucking yarn under a previous weaving when changing colors, glue the end of the yarn to the stick.

The results of this method are pleasing, but not as natural looking as when made with twigs.

75

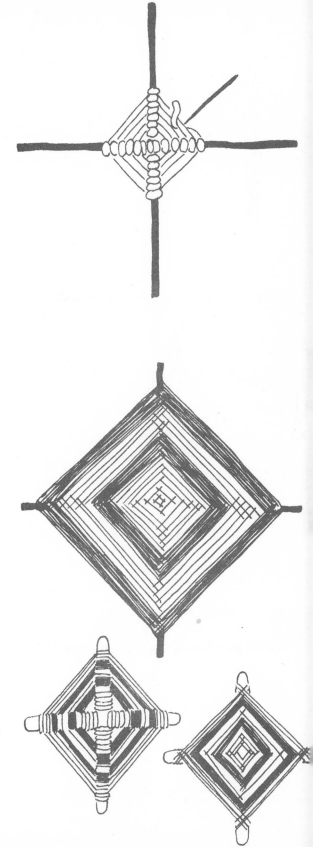

# 7

## Which A Witch?

It was a hot, sultry day in early August, the kind of day that seems to bring out the worst in people who find themselves in central New Jersey at that time of year. It hadn't rained for weeks. The crops were withering. The cows were giving little milk. The hens weren't laying, and worst of all, it was hard to breathe, or even think. A blanket of hot air covered the earth, with no breeze coming either from the ocean or the mountains. People felt smothered. Or at least, that's the way Justice Harkins felt, as he walked his horse slowly down Amwell road toward East Millstone, in the summer of 1692.

He looked down the road. An angry crowd had gathered at the posthouse. Even at a distance, he could hear them yelling, and he could see people pointing at someone, as Dame Miller, the innkeeper's wife, held a broom over her head. But the scene didn't make sense to the Justice. No one seemed to be holding a thief, or separating people who had been in a fight.

He strained his ears, and at last he caught above the din a word he dreaded to hear—"Witch!"

"Oh, no!" he thought. "Not in New Jersey!" As he rode

closer to the crowd, he understood the cry loud and clear: "Hetty Van Nuys is a witch!"

Some people were yelling, "Hang the witch!"

Others were shouting, "She's not a witch!"

The Justice stopped his horse at the edge of the crowd. All grew quiet.

"This is not the time or place for a trial," he said firmly. "But tell me. Why are you shouting?"

"Hetty Van Nuys is a witch!" cried Dame Miller. "She came to the posthouse begging salt. And then the butter wouldn't form in my churn."

"And my best cow got sick. She's never been sick before," added a farmer.

"Last spring my ewe gave birth to a lamb with two heads," said another. "Only a witch can cause a lamb to be born with two heads."

"How do you know that Hetty Van Nuys caused these misfortunes?" asked the Justice. "How do you know she's a witch?"

"Look at her!" demanded Dame Miller. "She looks like a witch. Folks from New England say they all look alike, those witches. Long nose, wisps of gray hair, clothes hanging loose on a bundle of bones. She looks like a witch!"

"Or like a frail old woman," asserted Dame Van Dyke, as she put an arm around the tiny, shabby woman standing next to her.

"Are you a witch?" asked the Justice, looking the old woman straight in the eye.

"No, I am not a witch," sobbed the woman. "I am Hetty

Van Nuys. I live in the hollow. I asked Dame Miller for salt, because they always have salt at the inn. But I am not a witch. I swear by all that is holy that I am not a witch!"

"If she swears by all that is holy that she is not witch, let her undergo the trial by Holy Book, and the trial by water," shouted Dame Miller.

"Let her undergo the trial by Holy Book, and the trial by water," echoed the crowd.

Dame Van Dyke held Hetty more closely, as a few other people gathered around the two women.

The Justice dismounted, walked to Hetty, placed his hand on hers, and said kindly, "What do you say, Hetty? What do you say about a trial?"

A new strength came to Hetty. A light shown in her eyes. She threw back her shoulders, lifted her head and said in a firm, if aged, voice, "I'll undergo any trial, if my accuser, Dame Miller, will take the same test."

"Fair enough!" exclaimed the Justice. "Everyone knows that Dame Miller is a God-fearing woman. If the trials are just, Dame Miller will pass the tests."

Of course, Dame Miller protested. She would lose time from her work at the inn. She would get wet being dunked into the river. She argued and she cried; but the judge held firm. It was fair, he claimed, for the accused and the accuser to undergo the same tests for witchcraft.

The crowd supported him.

The Justice set Thursday as the day for the trial to be held near the posthouse, on the banks of the Millstone River. Then he looked at the sky.

"Please excuse me," he said, as he mounted his horse.

"Black clouds are forming. I want to go home to enjoy the rain, if it comes."

"Me, too! Me, too!" cried the others, as they hurried away, leaving Dame Miller standing alone in front of the posthouse.

Thursday was a clear day, the kind that comes only after a long-awaited rain. People needed no urging to make Trial Day, as it was called, a holiday. Folks from miles around arrived early on horseback, on foot, and in wagons laden with food. They came prepared to spend the day.

After a good deal of lighthearted banter, they formed a huge circle around the largest scales in the county, brought to East Millstone for the trial by Holy Book.

At the appointed hour, the Justice appeared, followed by Dame Miller and Hetty Van Nuys. The Justice read the rules of the trial, and added that after the accused person had been put through a trial, the accuser would undergo the same test.

The minister put a large Bible on one side of the scale. Hetty Van Nuys was instructed to sit on the other side, to determine if the weight of the Devil would outweigh the weight of the Word of God.

Hetty sat down. The Bible bounced up and off the scales.

"Witch!" yelled the crowd. "The Devil outweighs the Holy Book."

The minister again placed the Bible on the scales. Dame Miller sat on the opposite side. Again the Bible bounced up and off the scales. The crowd was silent.

The Justice then explained the trial by water. "By tradition," he said, "a person is placed in a chair and dunked into a river. If she is a witch, she will bob up. If she is a God-fearing woman, she will sink."

"No! no! No!" screamed Dame Miller. "I am a God-fearing woman. I don't want to drown. Only a witch should face the trial by water."

"Are you asking me to make a prejudgment?" cautioned the Justice. "Dame Miller, we all know you are a God-fearing woman," he continued. "So today what is really on trial may be the method of testing an accused witch with the trial by book and the trial by water. Hetty Van Nuys, as is her right, has asked for a test. Proceed."

Hetty Van Nuys was placed in a chair and the chair was lowered into the Millstone River. Down went the chair and

Hetty Van Nuys. Up bobbed Hetty. Hetty was pulled from the water, and Dame Van Dyke threw a blanket around her.

Only a few in the crowd whispered, "Witch."

Then Dame Miller sat in the chair, after it had been dragged from the river. Down went the chair and Dame Miller. Up bobbed Dame Miller. She paddled to shore; dripping wet, she ran past the crowd into the posthouse.

The crowd roared. Dame Miller had asked for a trial by water, and she had got it! No one had to announce that either both women were God-fearing women, or both were witches.

"We'll have no more witch trials in the Millstone Valley. I'm sure of that," said Justice Harkins to himself, as he headed his horse toward home.

*(An incident that might have happened in colonial New Jersey)*

## Cornhusk Dolls

***Materials:*** dried corn husks;
heavy-duty tan thread; thin
wire; water; felt-tip pens

***Equipment:*** scissors; newspaper; plastic bag; string;
tweezers

To make a cornhusk doll, you
can use husks saved from garden
corn, dried husks from a field, or
husks purchased at an art supply
store.

To prepare the husks, discard
the heavy outer leaves. Cut off the
heavy stem ends and tips. If you
are using green corn husks,
spread them out on newspaper.
Cover them with three layers of
newspaper, and store in a hot or
warm place for a week or more.
They are ready when they look dry
and are no longer green.

Lay the husks you will use on a
newspaper, and sprinkle them
with water. They should be damp,
not wet. Put them in a plastic bag,
tie the top and leave overnight.
Husks ready to use should be
damp and flexible, but not wet.

To make a small doll, select 6
corn husks. Trim them so that they
are of equal length. Lay the husks
in a pile, with three large ends on
the right and three on the left.

Wrap a thread around the
middle of the bundle of husks. Pull

82

the bundle together as much as possible. Tie tightly.

Bring the two ends of the bundle of husks together, so that the thread is on top. Make sure that a flat unmarked husk is on the outside, as this is where the doll's face will be.

To make the head, wrap a thread around the bundle about 1 inch from the top. Pull the husks together tightly. Tie.

To make arms, choose one wide husk and run a small thin wire down its center, going in and out as if making long basting stiches. Choose four more husks. Lay them in a pile, with the husk containing the wire in the center. Wrap thread around the center of the bundle, and tie it. Wrap and tie thread near each end of the bundle, to make wrists.

Divide the husks under the head in half and slip the arm bundle between them. Push it up toward the head as far as possible. Adjust to make arms of equal length. Wrap thread around the husks under the arms, to make the waistline. Pull the bundle together as tightly as possible. Tie securely.

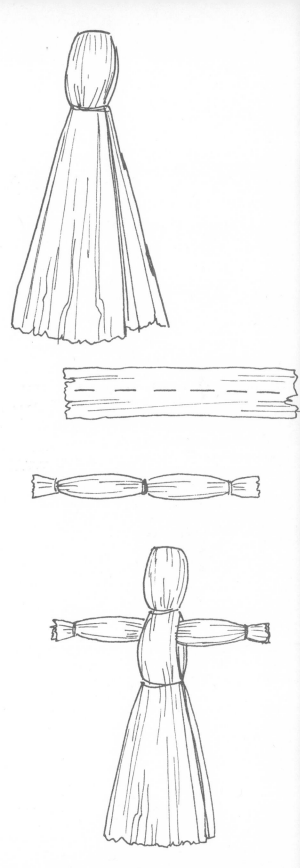

Cut narrow strips of husks. Wrap one strip a few times around the doll to make a waistband. Tie the ends. Do not try to pull the strips tight, or they will break. Using tweezers, tuck the ends under the waistband. Fluff out the cornhusks of the skirt. Trim them so they are even at the bottom. The doll should be able to stand alone.

Wrap strips of husks around the wrists and tie and tuck as at the waist.

Select a light-colored smooth husk for a bonnet. Place the center of one edge of this husk over the center of the doll's forehead. Drape the edge of the husk around the sides of the face, pulling the husk together at the back. Notice the peaked cap it makes.

Wrap a thread around the neck of the doll and the back of the bonnet. Pull as tightly as possible and tie. Cover this thread with a cornhusk strip, tied in front. Trim the ends of the bonnet in back and trim the bonnet tie.

Again, fluff out the skirt. Bend the arms the way you want them. They will dry in this position. Set the doll aside and let the husks dry thoroughly. A cornhusk doll does not need features, but if you

84

would like yours to have some, paint them on with felt-tip pens.

Now and then, in old New Jersey, someone burned a cornhusk doll made to represent a witch, in an effort to get rid of an evil spirit. However, cornhusk dolls were most commonly used as toys. They may be America's oldest type of doll, because many Indian tribes, as well as people in the colonies, made them for their children.

## Stenciled Name Plaque

**Materials:** piece of scrap lumber; heavy paper or stencil paper; latex paint; pencil; candle or paraffin wax; felt-tip pens; clear varnish; hanging hook

**Equipment:** small piece of sponge; sandpaper; paper towels; small dish or pan; scissors (or mat knife, if paper is very heavy)

Many people in colonial America became skilled in stenciling, the art of applying paint through a cutout design. They decorated furniture and other objects using this method.

To do stencil work, an artist makes a cutout stencil, or pattern, places the stencil on the object to be painted and, using either a sponge or stencil brush, dabs wet paint in the spaces. When the stencil is lifted, the pattern appears on the object being painted.

To decorate a name plaque with stencil designs, select a piece of scrap lumber on which you will be able to print your name and have a wide margin. Rub the wood with sandpaper until it is smooth. Wipe it clean.

Print your name with fat letters on a piece of paper, to arrange spacing. Then print it in pencil on

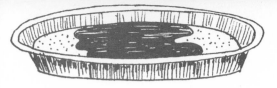

the prepared wood. Fill in the letters with colored felt-tip markers.

Design your stencil. Experiment with simple patterns of hearts, flowers, or geometric designs. A balanced design made by folding and cutting paper is the easiest. You can also make designs by cutting out the shapes with very sharp scissors or a mat knife.

When you have a pleasing design that can be repeated around the border of your plaque, draw it in the center of a small piece of heavy paper. Cut it out. Rub the top of the stencil paper with a piece of wax (paraffin or candle) to prevent paint from soaking into the paper. Place your cutout stencil on the wood where you want the pattern to start.

Prepare a paint pad by folding a paper towel several times to make a small pad. Put the pad in a shallow dish or pan. Pour paint on it until it is wet, but not resting in liquid. Press the sponge on the paint pad. If the sponge drips paint, press it lightly on another pad of paper toweling.

Dab paint through the cutout pattern in the stencil onto the wood. Lift the stencil. Let the paint dry before you stencil another design near it. Repeat, making

87

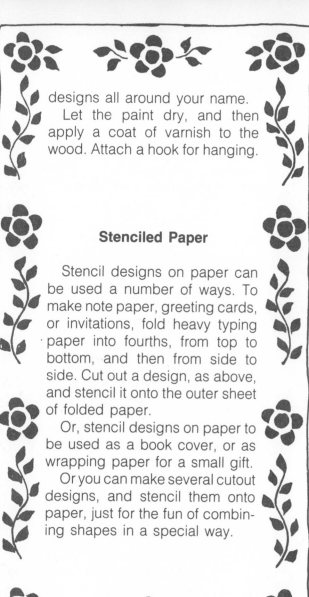

designs all around your name.

Let the paint dry, and then apply a coat of varnish to the wood. Attach a hook for hanging.

### Stenciled Paper

Stencil designs on paper can be used a number of ways. To make note paper, greeting cards, or invitations, fold heavy typing paper into fourths, from top to bottom, and then from side to side. Cut out a design, as above, and stencil it onto the outer sheet of folded paper.

Or, stencil designs on paper to be used as a book cover, or as wrapping paper for a small gift.

Or you can make several cutout designs, and stencil them onto paper, just for the fun of combining shapes in a special way.

# 8

## Big Long Man and the Giant

One day long ago, Big Long Man, the Navajo, went into the mountains where he met a giant, taller than the largest cedar tree, with fangs like a wolf.

"Aha! You will make a fine meal," said the giant. He picked up Big Long Man in one hand and put him in the basket which he had strapped to his back. Then he walked on toward his home in the canyon.

Big Long Man lay still, trying to think of a way to escape. Finally he called out, "Giant! Oh, Giant! I have something to tell you."

"What is it?" asked the Giant, sitting down on a rock pile.

"If you let me rest at every pile of rocks on the trail," said Big Long Man, "I will grow heavier and heavier, and you will have a bigger dinner."

"Is that so?" asked the Giant. "Hmmm." He sat for a bit and then walked on. He thought about what Big Long Man had said.

"I do like fat Navajos, the heavier the better," he said to himself. "There can't be any harm in trying the scheme." At the next pile of rocks, he set the basket on the ground.

"I will lie down a bit," he said to Big Long Man. "Get fatter, little cousin. Get fatter."

While Giant was resting, Big Long Man crawled out of the basket and put a rock under his shirt. Then he crept back into the basket.

"I am ready," he called to the Giant.

"My you are heavier, little cousin!" said Giant, when he picked up the basket. He lifted the lid and looked at Big Long Man, whose stomach bulged with the rock hidden under his shirt.

"Good! You will taste better," said Giant.

"Yes," said Big Long Man. "I get fatter every time you set me down."

Giant started off at a fast pace. He was in a hurry to get home and taste roast Navajo. At the next pile of rocks, he stopped and put the basket down again.

"Get fatter, little cousin. Get fatter," he said, and sat himself down for a rest.

Big Long Man crept out of the basket and hid another stone under his shirt. When he was safely inside the basket, he called out, "Giant. Oh, Giant. I am ready."

Giant strapped the basket to his back.

"My you are heavier!" he said. "You told the truth, little cousin. What a big dinner I'll have! How juicy you will taste."

He hurried down the path toward his home. After a bit, he set the basket down near another pile of rocks. Big Long Man crawled out of the basket and hid a third rock under his shirt. Once more he crawled into the basket, and Giant set off down the path.

Big Long Man knew they would soon be near the giant's home. He peeked out a crack in the basket. Presently, he saw the giant's house, as tall as a cliff, in front of them.

"Set me down again, Giant," he called. "I need to get a bit fatter."

"Hurry, little Navajo!," said the giant, setting the basket down a fourth time. "My wife is waiting at the door."

Big Long Man said to himself, "I must run now, or be put onto the roasting stick." He crept out and put one more big rock into the basket. Then he closed the lid and hid behind a cedar tree.

The giant picked up the basket of rocks. "Oh, you are heavy, Navajo," groaned Giant, as he strapped the

91

basket to his back and went plodding down the path. When he reached home, his wife was standing at the door.

"Wife." he called, "Look at the fine dinner I brought you. A tender fat Navajo."

He unstrapped the basket and handed it to his wife.

"Good," cried Mrs. Giant, "I'm hungry. I'll cook him right away!" She dumped the basket upside down on the floor. Bang! Bang! The rocks fell into a pile at her feet. Mrs. Giant flew into a rage.

"Stupid! Stupid! Stupid!" she cried. "A fine Navajo you caught!"

"What's the matter?" asked Giant.

"Nice tender rocks for our dinner!" shrieked Mrs. Giant.

Giant scratched his head and turned the rocks over. "The Navajo turned into stone," he said. "Too bad. Too bad."

"Turned into stone, did he?" cried Mrs. Giant. "You idiot! He tricked you. He jumped out and filled the basket with rocks. What a fool I have for a husband."

Giant gnashed his teeth. He roared, "I'll get him! I'll get that Navajo! He will be my dinner yet." He ran out of the house and went to every rock pile where he had rested the basket.

He called, "Navajo, where are you? Navajo, come here!"

Giant's voice was like thunder. Big Long Man heard him shouting, but by this time, he was far away across the canyon, safe and sound.

*(A Navajo tale)*

## Sand Painting

**Materials:** dry, clean sand; powdered tempera paints; household glue; pencil; cardboard; water

**Equipment:** scrap paper; crayons; paintbrush; small can or dish to hold diluted glue; containers for sand; newspaper

Make a picture of Big Long Man and his wife in a sand painting, or copy a pattern from a Navajo rug, choosing the earth colors that Navajos use: grays, browns, black, and brick red. First draw the picture or design on scrap paper. Keep it simple. Color it, so that you will know later just where to put each color sand. Then transfer your drawing to a piece of cardboard, but do not color it.

Cover your workspace with newspaper. Using a separate container for each color, put from 2 to 4 tablespoons of sand in each one. Add dry tempera paint and mix it well with the sand until you have the colors you want. If your background cardboard is not brown, you may want to leave some sand uncolored.

Dilute a small amount of household glue with an equal amount of water. Using a paintbrush, put glue on one small section of the drawing. Sprinkle the proper

93

color sand on this area. Let the extra sand fall off onto newspaper. Paint each area with glue and sand until the picture is complete.

If you have more colored sand than you need for one project, you can store it in airtight containers for use at some future time.

## Nature Weaving

**Materials:** heavy cardboard; string, twine, or crochet cotton for the warp thread (yarn may also be used for the weft); dry grasses, weeds, wheat, feathers; twigs

**Equipment:** scissors; ruler; pencil

Navajos are, and have been for centuries, skilled weavers. Although their rugs and blankets usually follow basic patterns, and the weavers use the traditional earth colors of brown, gray, black, and brick red, and sometimes a touch of turquoise and yellow, the best of today's weavers show much creativity in putting old designs together in new ways.

Making a nature weaving that can be used as a wallhanging will give you a chance to use old skills

94

and create a new design. Collect a few nature items that can be woven into a hanging, such as wide grasses, a stalk of wheat, a long feather. Assemble more of these than you think you'll use, so you can have a choice as you work.

Make a loom, using a piece of cardboard the size you want your finished weaving to be. Draw a 1-inch margin on the top and bottom. Measure 1 inch from each side along the top line, and mark the spots. Then mark off every ½ inch between these spots. Mark the bottom line in the same way.

Cut ½-inch slits in the cardboard at each point you have marked.

Now string the warp (the vertical threads that form the skeleton for the body of weaving). Start by wrapping string (or whatever material you have chosen) around the cardboard at the top left-hand margin. Pull it through the first slit, from back to front. Bring the string down to the slit directly below it at the bottom. Pull it through to the back of the cardboard and over to the nearest slit at the bottom. Pull it through this slit to the front of the cardboard, and then up to the second slit on the top row. Continue to string the loom in this

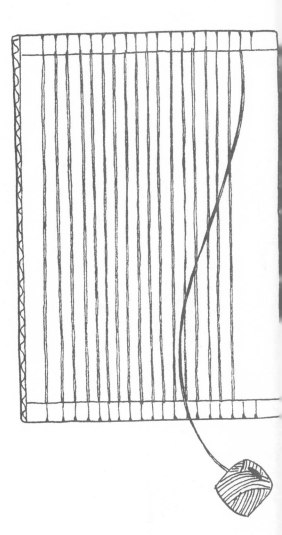

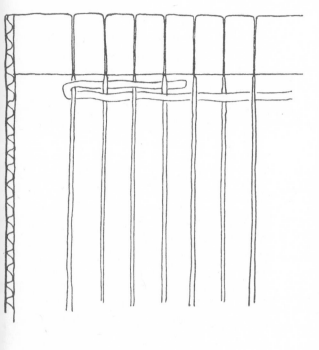

way until all the slits are filled. Fasten the end of the thread.

This is your loom. You are ready to weave.

Cut a piece of yarn about an arm's length, a workable length for a beginning weaver. You can add more yarn of the same color if you need it. This yarn will form the weft (the horizontal threads of weaving).

Don't tie the weft to the warp. Start to weave three or four spaces in from the margin on the left side of the top and weave to the left margin. This locks the thread in place and there are no unsightly knots (see diagram).

Then begin to weave the weft. Weave over and under, over and under the warp thread. Now weave the second row. If you went over a thread in the first row, go under it in the second row. In plain weaving, each row is the opposite of the row above it.

As you weave, push your weft threads close together. Each row of threads holds the row before it in place.

After you have finished an inch or more of weaving, fasten your yarn by weaving the end a few

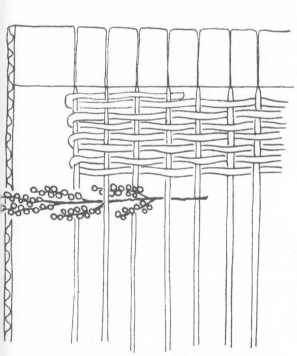

96

spaces back into the warp. Then weave in an interesting piece of weed or grass.

You can continue with the same yarn you have been using, or change color, or change to a thread of a different texture. Experiment to produce an original and pleasing hanging. Weave in other nature items when you wish.

When you reach the bottom of the loom, fasten your thread by weaving the end back into the woven fabric.

Choose a nearly straight twig a little longer than the weaving is wide. As you remove the loops from the top of the loom, slip them over the twig. Do the same with another twig at the bottom.

Cut a piece of yarn a little longer than the hanging is wide. Tie the ends of the yarn to the ends of the top stick.

Now your nature weaving is ready to hang.

# 9

## Juan Malo and His Magic Rod

Juan Malo was a rascal, no two ways about it, and the royal governor from Spain was a rogue in his own way. Each thought he had a perfect right to take advantage of the other whenever he could.

"I am Chamorro," Juan Malo would tell his beloved carabao (his water buffalo), or any other creature that would seem to listen. "My people have lived on the island of Guam since before the time of our ancestors.

"The Spaniard is a newcomer. He rules the island with weapons. But we Chamorro control the island with wit." By "wit," Juan Malo meant quick thinking, and sometimes tricks, to let the Spaniard know that he was not all-mighty. There was no room in Chamorro hearts for mean hatred.

"I am the magistrate," the governor of the island would say to himself, because no one else would listen to him. "I was sent here by the King of Spain to turn these lazy natives into industrious Spaniards, making money for the crown. That's impossible! They're too lazy. But if I can take advantage of the situation, keep these simple people in their place, and make a little money for myself, so be it." By "keeping people in their place" the governor meant taking advantage of Juan Malo and his friends. There was no room in the governor's heart for the idea of human equality.

Most of the time, Juan Malo and the governor kept a goodly distance apart. The governor stayed close to the palace, the coolest place on the island. And Juan Malo stayed in his village, or the wild land around it.

But once in a while, the governor got on his magnificent horse and rode into the countryside. And once in a while, Juan Malo let his beloved old carabao wander down the road that led to the palace. Juan Malo never drove his carabao. The animal knew, better than the master, where they both wanted to go—and there they went.

One time, the carabao went right to the palace gate. Juan Malo thought, "I must be here for some reason," so he asked the governor to give him a job. The last thing the governor wanted was to have Juan Malo working near the palace—or for that matter, standing around the palace demanding work. His first idea was to get Juan Malo and his carabao as far away from the palace as possible, as quickly as possible. So he gave him a coin and told him to watch the three little pigs in a distant pasture.

Juan Malo took the coin, rode off on the back of his carabao, and obeyed orders. He watched the little pigs as they wandered into an open field. He watched them as he made a hopeless attempt to get them back into the pasture. He watched them as he killed them, roasted them, ate them, and buried their skeletons in the mud, with feet sticking up. Juan Malo reasoned that, after all, the governor had a right to find out what had happened to his pigs, but why stay around to tell him? His job done, Juan Malo mounted his carabao and returned to his village.

When the governor discovered what had happened to his pigs, he was furious and ordered his soldiers to arrest Juan Malo—if they happened to see him. But that was long ago.

On the day our story took place, Juan Malo had almost forgotten about the governor and his soldiers. He was turning his thoughts to a stick that he had cut from a banyan tree, and to all his worldly wealth, two reales, tied in a rag and tucked under his waistband.

He was on the back of his carabao, jogging slowly, very slowly, down Sumay-Piti road, in the hot noonday sun.

As was his custom, Juan Malo began to contemplate. "Here I have nothing but the stick of a banyan tree. If I were smart, I could have a fortune from it. If I put the branch of a banyan tree in the ground, another branch will grow from it. All things multiply. Isn't that so, Friend Carabao?" He gave the carabao a smart slap on the rump, but the carabao jogged down the road, neither agreeing nor disagreeing with his master.

"But do I need another banyan tree?" Juan Malo asked himself.

Then he took the two reales from the rag tucked under his waistband. "Now the governor's reales are like my banyan tree. When I stick the banyan branch into the ground, it multipies. When the governor puts reales in his purse, they multiply until his purse can't hold them. Then he puts them in a chest, where they multiply more and more.

"Now why should my two reales remain two reales? If I stick them in the earth like a banyan branch, they ought to multiply. Isn't that so, Friend Carabao?" The carabao gave no answer.

"No wonder you can't figure it out, Friend Carabao. That's a lot of thinking for today. The sun is hot. The sea looks restful. It's time for my siesta."

So saying, he dismounted and lay down on the beach. Then the carabao, as was his custom, ambled across the sand, leaving deep footprints as he walked, and waded into the water. Juan Malo looked at the footprints, dropped one of his reales into a hole, covered the coin with sand, and planted his banyan stick on top of it.

"Maybe it will multiply," he said dreamily. "Maybe."

He was about to fall asleep, when he heard the sound of hoofbeats. He opened his eyes and looked up. There directly above him, seated on a horse, was the governor!

"Oh, no!" thought Juan Malo, without blinking an eye. "The Governor! He's got me now. Or has he? Without his soldiers, has he?" Juan Malo slowly turned his head and looked at his stick.

No one spoke for a minute or more. At last the governor shouted, "Juan Malo!"

"Yes, Your Excellency," Juan Malo replied.

"I should have you arrested."

"Yes, Your Excellency."

"But I have no soldiers with me."

"I see, Your Excellency."

"So tell me, why are you sitting and looking at a stick?"

"Watching, Your Excellency," Juan Malo explained. "Watching my magic money-making rod."

"Money-making rod?"

"Yes, Your Excellency. Come watch with me."

The governor's curiosity was greater than his anger with Juan Malo. He got off his horse and stood by the stick.

"Your Excellency," Juan Malo explained, "my magic rod is growing money."

"Growing money?" The idea was too much for the governor, who loved money dearly and felt that he would give anything for a magic rod, or anything else that would grow money.

"Show me how your stick grows money," he commanded.

"Yes, Your Excellency," said Juan Malo, rising slowly and looking at the sun. "The time is right. I will show you." Juan Malo walked toward his stick, and without turning his head, dropped his remaining coin into a second footprint left by his carabao.

The governor kept his eyes glued to the magic stick.

"See, I shall lift my magic rod." There in the sand lay a coin. Juan picked it up. "Look, Your Excellency."

"I see. This is most unusual," admitted the governor. "No doubt. . . ."

"Oh, if you doubt," offered Juan Malo, "I'll put my rod in another spot. He casually put his stick on top of his second coin, half buried in the sand.

"Now," instructed Juan Malo, "pull out my magic rod."

The governor grabbed the stick, pulled it out of the sand, and spotted the coin. "Incredible!" he exclaimed. "I must have this magic rod."

"Oh, no, Your Excellency," wailed Juan Malo. "Please do not take my magic rod. It's my only source of income. You know I am poor. You know I don't work well."

The governor glared at him, knowing all too well what Juan meant.

"This magic rod," said the governor, with all the pomp and authority he could muster, "belongs in the hands of a wise man, not in the possession of an ignorant lazybones."

"In that case," said Juan Malo, humbly, "I must accept your wise judgment. But please, Your Grace, will you buy my magic rod, and not just take it from me? I'll sell it for thirty reales, a bargain."

"Twenty!" said the governor as he tossed coins in the sand.

"Thank you, Your Excellency," said Juan Malo, picking up the coins.

"Thank you for buying my magic rod," he added, as he pulled his carabao out of the water and mounted. Then he turned to the governor to give him one piece of advice.

"One thing you should understand, Your Excellency. You can gather reales only when the sun is directly over that niyog tree in which my Taotamona lives. It is too late today for my magic rod to grow more reales. See, the sun has passed the peak. So meet me here tomorrow. Then I'll address my Taotamona for you and show you how to use the magic rod."

"Agreed," said the governor.

"Then," added Juan Malo, "because you are a generous man, you will give me one more real for my bother."

Juan Malo and his carabao set off for the country. They did not return the next day, or on the days that followed.

But the governor arrived the next day at the appointed spot, just as the sun was high above the niyog tree. He put the stick into the sand, waited, removed the rod—no coin. Again and again he experimented. Day after day, he returned to the spot, sticking his rod into the sand here and there. After a week, he realized that Juan Malo had outwitted him again.

But this time, he did not direct his soldiers to arrest Juan

Malo. In fact, he kept the whole story to himself. He felt very foolish.

"And yet," he used to say to himself, "it would be nice to have a magic rod that grows money. For twenty reales, it would be worth it. How did Juan Malo find that second coin in the sand? Did he grow it? With some island magic, did he grow it?"

*(A Chamorro tale from Guam, retold)*

## Slot Sculpture

**Materials:** lightweight cardboard such as cereal box, suit box, or manila file folder; scrap paper; pencil; crayons or paints
**Equipment:** scissors, paintbrush

Slot sculpture is the art of making slots in parts of a figure and putting the parts together by inserting one piece into the slot of another. This gives a three-dimensional figure.

Practice slotting by putting together two squares of lightweight cardboard. To make a slot, cut a triangle with a base as wide as the cardboard is thick. Being accurate about this width will produce joints that fit and hold. Make a slot from the top of one square of cardboard to its center. Make a slot from the bottom of the other square to its center. Put the two pieces together. They should stand at right angles to each other. This is the basic method for making a slot figure.

In making a slot sculpture of an animal, cut out one part of the body, side view, and the other parts of the body, front view. But first, draw a pattern on scrap paper, and then transfer it to cardboard.

Draw and cut out the body of Juan Malo's carabao, side view.

106

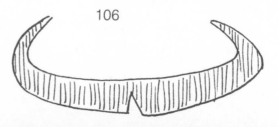

Draw and cut out the front legs, including the part of the body between the legs, front view. Draw and cut out an identical pair of legs for the hind legs. Cut slots in the bottom of the body and in the top center of each pair of legs. Attach the legs to the body.

Draw and cut out, all in one piece, two long horns, front view, thick in the center. Cut slots in the top of the head and in the bottom of the horn piece. Put together. Draw and cut out a tail. Cut slots in the top end of the tail and the rump of the carabao. Put together.

To make a figure of Juan to go astride his carabao, draw and cut out a front-view figure of the body of a man without arms. Cut a slot in the back of the carabao and one between the legs of the man. Put the figures together. Draw and cut out two arms. Make a slot in the top of each shoulder of the man, and up from the bottom of the upper part of each arm. Put the pieces together.

You can display your sculpture as it is. Or you can take it apart, paint it, and reassemble it.

You can make other slot-sculpture figures: the Spanish governor on his horse, Juan Malo kneeling in the sand, a palm tree, a tropical bird, or something else that suits your fancy.

107

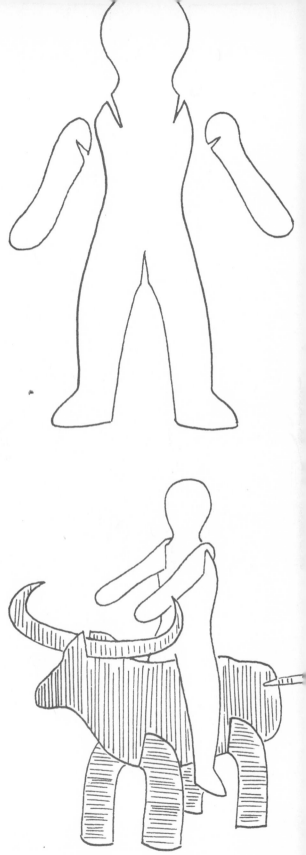

## Shell Pictures

***Materials:*** shells; heavy-duty household glue; background material suitable for shells; frame if desired

Many people on the island of Guam collect beautiful shells they find on the beaches and use them to create pictures. Some artists make pictures using only shells. Others combine shells and other objects found along the shore, such as dried grass, bits of driftwood, and small pieces of net. Some combine painting and shellcraft.

Choose a background material suitable for your art work and strong enough to support the shells you want to use. If you are making a small card to put on top of a gift, use very small shells, and glue them on a card with a glossy finish. For a plaque, use varnished plywood, cork, or bristol board for your background.

Wash and dry your shells. Arrange them on the background. Glue them in place, using heavy-duty household glue.

Many shell pictures need no frames. Others are framed with rope or other material glued into place. Some have traditional frames.

### Decorated Box

***Additional Materials:*** small
wooden box

Buy a small wooden box, large
enough to hold bobby pins, paper
clips, or some other small objects.
Varnish it. Decorate the top with a
shell design.

# 10

## One Man's Horse

One day the Caliph Haroun-al-Raschid disguised himself and left his palace in Baghdad to travel through his country and see for himself how his people fared. Mounted on a fine steed, he traveled on until he came to within a few miles of the town of Bassora. There he saw a poor cripple seated by the wayside.

"An alms! An alms! I beg of you," implored the beggar.

The caliph threw him a piece of money, and was about to ride on, when a sudden thought stopped him. "Old beggar," he said, "to what city do you journey?"

"To the city of Bassora," answered the cripple.

Dismounting, the caliph helped the old man to the horse's back, then mounting in front of him, rode into Bassora.

Arriving at their journey's end, the caliph said to the cripple, "Dismount. I leave you here."

"Dismount yourself," answered the beggar. "The horse is mine."

"What!" cried the caliph. "Miserable beggar! Did I not lift you from the roadside?"

"Very true," replied the beggar, "but can you prove it?

In Bassora we are both strangers. It is your word against mine. What are you going to do?"

That was a question the caliph had to answer for himself. He thought, "If I throw the old man into the gutter, he will cry out. A mob will gather and yell, 'Give the old man his horse!'

"If I give the thief a large sum of money, he'll be glad to let me have my horse and at the same time be encouraged to cheat someone else in the same way.

"If I ask a judge to settle the case, I may lose my horse; but at the same time, I'll find out how the cadi of Bassora deals justice."

So the disguised caliph turned to the wretched beggar and said, "Come, then, we will go to the cadi. You tell your story, and I'll tell mine. We will leave the matter in his hands."

So saying, they went to the place where the cadi was holding court. Two men stood before the cadi: an oil merchant, and a porter. The porter held a piece of gold in his hand. "This coin," he said, "belongs to me."

"Your Honor," said the oil merchant, "That coin is mine. I have owned it for many years and always carry it. I lost it only today."

"Are there any witnesses?" asked the cadi.

"No, Your Honor," answered the man.

"Very well," said the cadi, "Leave the coin with me and return tomorrow."

"That's a queer way to render justice," thought the caliph to himself.

111

The next case was called, and two other men approached the cadi.

"What is your trade?" he asked the first.

"I am a writer," was the answer.

"Why are you here?" continued the cadi.

"This morning while I was at prayer at the mosque, someone stole my copy of the Koran. That tailor," he said pointing to the other man, "now has it and claims that it is his."

"Are there any witnesses?"

"None, Your Honor," replied the man.

"Very well," said the cadi, "Leave the book with me and return tomorrow."

"That's a strange way to render justice," again thought the caliph.

Next the cadi called the caliph and beggar before him.

"Who are you? And what is your trouble?" he asked, addressing the caliph.

"Your Honor," replied the caliph, "I am a traveler from Baghdad. A few miles from your city gates, I met this crippled beggar lying by the wayside. I had compassion on him, and lifting him to my horse's back, brought him to this city. He repays my kindness with the basest ingratitude. He claims that my horse is his own."

The cadi then turned to the beggar. "What have you to say in answer to this man's charge?" he said.

"The horse is mine," answered the beggar. "I raised him from a colt, and we love each other as brothers. If my horse is taken from me, what shall I do? You see, I am a poor cripple, and I need my faithful horse to carry me."

112

Here the old beggar pretended to weep to gain the sympathy of the judge.

"Bless me," thought the caliph to himself, "How is the cadi going to decide? The old humbug almost persuades me that I have stolen my own horse."

The cadi calmly asked, "Have you any witnesses?"

"No, Your Honor," replied the caliph and the beggar.

"Then," said the cadi, "leave the horse with one of my soldiers for the night, and return to this courtroom tomorrow morning."

The next morning, the caliph arrived at the courtroom early, for he was eager to hear how the cadi would decide all the cases.

Promptly at the opening hour, the cadi entered the room, and at once called the oil merchant and the porter

before him. Handing the gold piece to the merchant, he said, "Here is your gold piece. Take it and depart."

Then he turned to the porter. "You have tried to keep what did not belong to you, and you have lied," he said in a stern voice.

"Soldiers," he called, "Take this man from the courtroom, and give him twenty strokes with a rod on the soles of his bare feet."

Next the writer and the tailor came before him. "This book, I find, belongs to the writer," he said. "I now return it to him."

"Soldiers, take this false-swearing tailor, and give him thirty lashes with whips on the palms of his hands."

At last the caliph and the beggar were called before the cadi, who addressed the beggar: "Why hast thou repaid kindness with ingratitude? Do you not know that the ungrateful man is the most miserable wretch on earth? Since you are a cripple, I will not have you beaten, but will keep you in prison until you repent of your evil ways.

"Good traveler, the horse is yours. Take it, and continue on your way. May your kindness be better rewarded in the future."

The caliph thanked the judge and stepped to the back of the room. There he waited, until all but the cadi had left the courtroom. Then he approached him and said, "Honored Judge, I much admire your wisdom. Without doubt, the spirit of the prophet inspired you. How else could you render such righteous judgments?"

"These cases have all been very simple," replied the cadi. "Did you not hear the oil merchant say that he had carried that piece of gold for many years? Last night I threw the coin into a glass of clear water. This morning, I found the surface of the water covered with tiny drops. I then knew, beyond doubt, that the coin belonged to the oil merchant."

"Good," said the caliph, "But pray tell me how you knew to whom the Koran belonged?"

"That case was equally easy to settle," responded the cadi. "On examining the book, I found that the pages most used were those on which the duties of writers and scholars were set forth. The book belonged to the writer."

"Your judgment is most excellent!" exclaimed the caliph. "But how could you tell to whom the horse belonged?"

"Last night I had your horse put in a stable that you and the beggar would have to pass on your way to court today. This morning I went to the stable. When the beggar passed, the horse never looked up. But when you passed the open door, he stretched out his head and neighed as horses do only when a loved master approaches. So you see, my friend, the matter was very simple after all."

"Simple!" cried the caliph. "Your wisdom equals that of Solomon! I am the Caliph Haroun-al-Raschid. I need just such a man as you in my capital city. Honest Judge, I now make you Grand Cadi of Baghdad."

*(A Turkish tale)*

## Shadow Puppets and Theater

***Materials:*** thin cardboard, such as manila file folder, suit box, or oaktag; colored cellophane or tissue paper; staples; sturdy lightweight wire; wooden frame or large carton; white tissue paper or cloth, such as a piece of worn sheet; light glue

***Equipment:*** scissors; stapler

Nobody knows just who brought shadow puppets to Turkey, but records show they have been attracting crowds since the fourteenth century. The two best-known characters, Karaghioz, a rascally stone mason, and his friend Hachivat, are constantly fighting and poking fun at whoever is in authority.

Turkish shadow puppets are simple and bold in design, about a foot high, and made of stiff material. One unusual feature is the way color is added.

You can have traditional puppets discuss conditions today, or you can make characters for a story. To make a puppet, draw and cut out of cardboard the side view of a character running, with one arm extended. Then cut out portions of the clothing where you want color, leaving a frame around the edge. Staple brightly colored tissue paper or cellophane over the openings.

116

Hook a sturdy, lightweight wire over a staple near the top of the puppet's body. Staple the wire in place on the puppet's foot, allowing the end of the wire to extend below the figure.

For a shadow puppet theater, you need a frame with a piece of tissue paper or thin white cloth stretched across the opening. The frame may be a wooden one, or a cardboard carton with a large hole cut in one side.

To operate a puppet, sit below the screen and hold the puppet up by the wire, between the screen and a light behind it. Remember to keep your body and hand below the stage, so that only the puppet is in the path of the light. Experiment to find out where and how to place the light, and how high, and how close to the screen, to hold the puppet. Shadow puppets grow larger or smaller as they are moved toward the screen or away from it.

As you plan your play, do not crowd your stage with characters. Each figure must stand alone, because one figure behind another won't show.

You can attach scenery to the top of the stage—sun, moon, bird, or even a towering sunflower, but don't clutter your stage, because a puppet won't show if it gets in front of, or behind, scenery.

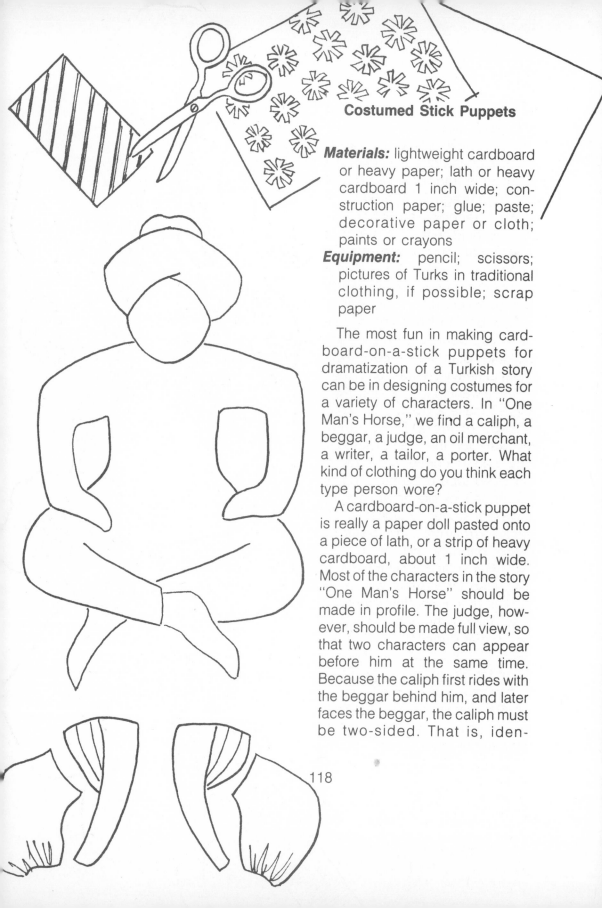

## Costumed Stick Puppets

**Materials:** lightweight cardboard or heavy paper; lath or heavy cardboard 1 inch wide; construction paper; glue; paste; decorative paper or cloth; paints or crayons

**Equipment:** pencil; scissors; pictures of Turks in traditional clothing, if possible; scrap paper

The most fun in making cardboard-on-a-stick puppets for dramatization of a Turkish story can be in designing costumes for a variety of characters. In "One Man's Horse," we find a caliph, a beggar, a judge, an oil merchant, a writer, a tailor, a porter. What kind of clothing do you think each type person wore?

A cardboard-on-a-stick puppet is really a paper doll pasted onto a piece of lath, or a strip of heavy cardboard, about 1 inch wide. Most of the characters in the story "One Man's Horse" should be made in profile. The judge, however, should be made full view, so that two characters can appear before him at the same time. Because the caliph first rides with the beggar behind him, and later faces the beggar, the caliph must be two-sided. That is, identical paper dolls should be glued onto each side of the stick.

If you have books available, study pictures of Turkish people dressed in traditional clothing of many years ago. Draw a sketch of a character on scrap paper. The figure should be at least 10 inches tall, so that you can show details of clothing. Trace and cut out your basic drawing from thin cardboard or very heavy paper.

Now decide what kind of material you want to use in making clothing. Start with a basic garment of heavy contruction paper.

If you want to work entirely with paper, make a collage by using scraps of metallic paper or giftwrap for the main garment. You can decorate with bits of gummed tape or strips of bright paper, to look like embroidery or jewels or woven designs.

Or you may choose to cover the basic garment with cloth. The beggar's outfit, for example, can be burlap. Or you may want to use scraps of iron-on cloth, covering only parts of the basic construction-paper garment.

Or you may want to color or paint the costume.

Whatever you decide to do, lay all the small pieces in place before you start to glue, paste, or iron any of them down.

When the garment for the puppet is complete, glue it onto the basic cardboard figure. Then glue the entire figure onto a piece of lath or a strip of heavy cardboard that extends below the puppet, giving the puppeteer a handle for working the puppet. Set the puppet aside until the glue is firm.

You do not need a theater for these puppets, since you can sit or stand behind any kind of barrier.

If you are more interested in art work than in dramatics, do not glue your figures onto sticks, but display them.

## Felt Wallhanging or Pillow Cover (with balanced design)

**Materials:** two squares of felt of different colors; thread in contrasting color

**Equipment:** scrap paper; sharp scissors; straight pins; needle; sewing machine with zigzag attachments, if available

Look at a Turkish rug, or a picture of one. Note how the design on the left-hand side is repeated on the right. You'll find this symmetry, or balance, in many types of Turkish art. If you make a wallhanging or pillow cover with your own duplicated pattern, you, too, will produce art work with a symmetrical design.

Choose two pieces of felt in contrasting, but harmonious, colors. You can use precut squares often sold in fabric shops, or cut your own. Squares with sides measuring 6 to 8 inches are a workable size.

To make a pattern, cut a square of scrap paper the same size as the felt square. Fold it in quarters. Snip out sections here and there on the fold. Keep the design bold and simple, for later, you will have

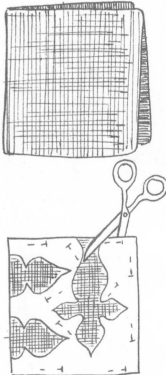

121

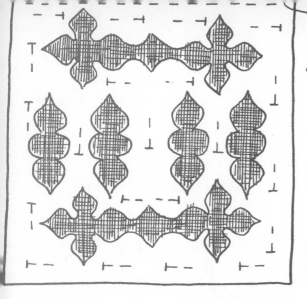

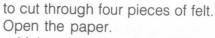

to cut through four pieces of felt. Open the paper.

Make several patterns. When you get one with a really clear, sharp design, fold a square of felt in quarters. Pin the folded paper design on the folded felt. Cut the felt slowly and carefully, making sure you have a clear-cut design before removing the pattern and opening the felt square.

Pin the cutout felt square onto the other felt square. Thread a needle and knot the end of the thread. Begin at one corner to sew a running stich, by bringing the needle from the back to the front of the felt, moving the needle forward and then putting it back through the fabric. Move the needle forward and begin again. Continue in this way, making evenly spaced stitches in a straight line. After you have stitched around the outside of the design, stitch the center portions.

You can use your felt design as a decoration. Or you can make a pillow cover with one large felt design, or by sewing together four or more smaller ones, using the zigzag attachment on a sewing machine.

Or you can create a really unusual wallhanging. Sew together a number of cut-felt designs, using the zigzag attachment. Attach tab loops at the top

and suspend the wallhanging from a rod. Several people might like to work together, making a wallhanging to be displayed in a special place, or given as a gift to a leader, or some other friend.

# Index

# INDEX

# INDEX

# QUICK WITS AND NIMBLE FINGERS